CALIFORNIA LANDSCAPE STANDARDS

California Landscape Standards
CLS

California Landscape Standards Committee
Chairman, Roger D. Fiske

California Landscape Contractors Association
Sacramento, California

The authors of this book, the Landscape Standards Committee, and the California Landscape Contractors Association assume no responsibility for the accuracy of this document and, additionally, assume no responsibility for results attributable to its use. Information contained herein is believed to be reliable; however, the contents are not to be construed as a representation that any of the materials or installation procedures are suited for a specific application. Information is suggestive only, and users must verify and determine the suitability of the information for their own purposes. Conformity to these standards does not ensure compliance with applicable ordinances, building codes, laws, and regulations.

Grateful acknowledgement is made for permission to reprint
the lumber sizing charts from *How To Design & Build Decks & Patios*
Copyright 1979
Ortho Information Services
Chevron Chemical Company
Consumer Products Division
P. 0. Box 5047
San Ramon, CA 94583

First Edition

Landscaping is the transformation of the natural features or appearance of a land space into a unified, esthetically pleasing, and functional human environment.

Landscape construction, the art and technology of landscaping, is unique in the construction industry. Involving a great diversity of crafts, landscape construction includes all improvements to a land space with the exception of building structures.

Many elements must be coordinated to create a landscape, including clearing and sculpting the land; providing proper and adequate drainage; construction of hardscape improvements such as wood decks and arbors, concrete patios and walks, masonry walls and paving; installation of proper irrigation systems; lighting for safety and nighttime enjoyment; and planting. Lastly, quality maintenance provides the care necessary to sustain the landscape.

The need for uniform minimum standards within the California landscape industry has long been recognized. To accomplish this goal, participation of representatives from all segments of the landscape industry was needed. The California Landscape Contractors Association agreed to underwrite costs of writing and publishing the standards.

All associations directly or indirectly related to the landscape industry were invited to participate in the project. With a positive response, the California Landscape Standards Committee was founded.

Writing of the standards has spread over many years, but at long last, the efforts of the many individuals who worked together on this undertaking have resulted in publication of the California Landscape Standards.

The contributions by members of the following organizations made the writing of the standards possible: American Institute of Architects, American Society of Golf Course Architects, American Society of Irrigation Consultants, American Society of Civil Engineers, American Society of Landscape Architects, Associated General Contractors, Associated Landscape Contractors of America, American Wood Preservers Institute, California Landscape Contractors Association, California Association of Nurserymen, California Redwood Association, California Turfgrass Council, Engineering and Grading Contractors Association, Interior Plantscape Association, Irrigation Association, Northern California Turfgrass Council, Portland Cement Association, Pressure Treated Products Association, Southern California Readymix Association, Southern California Turfgrass Council, and Western Wood Products Association.

As chairman of the Landscape Standards Committee, I wish to express my sincere appreciation to the many individuals who volunteered their time and energy to this effort.

First, I would like to recognize the individuals who directed and coordinated the section subcommittees: Keith Braman, Larry Carducci, Bob Crowell, Ken Gerlack, Robert Graves, Lebo Newman, Roger Northrup, Richard Reasoner, Carole Senter, Wendel Sonoda, and Marvin Weitzenhoffer.

I also thank the following committee members who contributed to the writing of the individual sections: Bob Anthis, Mai Arbegast, Walt Bray, Michael Brief, Dave Burnley, Bruce Camenga, Robert Carter, Allen Chariton, Steve Cockerhan, John Deming, Dave Dorward, Dennis Dougherty, Ed Duling, Tom Ellington, Robert Flood, John Gachina, M. E. Gardener, Jerry Gates, Tom Gee, Nancy Goldstein, Andy Gotzenberg, Dave Gutru, Doug Hanover, George Heinrichs, Gary Houck, Pete Howes, Emery Hunter, Owen James, Peter Johnson, George Juilly, Ken Jurgens, Mike Keller, Keith Kersell, Doug Ketchum, Ken Kline, Dick Lahey, Don Laughlin, Sandy Lee, Bill Locklin, David Marsh, Joe Marsh, Don Michaely, Russ Mitchell, Jack Moore, David McLeroy, Frank Peccorini, Bill Pogue, Wayne Richards, Chet Sarsfield, Allen Secrest, Herr Smith, Jim Synder, Robert Tobin, Rockwell Troth, Dennis Tsuboi, John Van Dam, John Vierra, Dean White, Ed Wilkinson, Steve Winkel, Phil Wyatt, and Steve Yam.

In addition, my thanks to Curtis Lee CSI for helping to establish the format of the standards; to Kenneth A. Andrew ASLA, Peter R. Dilallo ASLA, Ronald E. Hodges ASLA, Frederic J. Klemeyer Jr. AIA, Dr. Jack R. Lewis, and Dr. William Noble, who reviewed or contributed to the final drafts; and to Michael Hradecky ASLA, for the preparation and drawing of the details.

Participation of representatives from the California Department of Transportation, the California Department of Parks and Recreation, and the University of California Agricultural Cooperative Extension is also appreciated.

Very special thanks are due Anthony Amato, professor emeritus at California Polytechnic State University, San Luis Obispo, who coordinated the final efforts of this project. He assembled and compiled the final drafts from the subcommittees, spent countless hours editing, and made all of the arrangements for printing of the standards.

Finally, I express gratitude to my wife, Candy, who worked on the standards from beginning to end. Without her organizational, formatting and editing skills, as well as her dedication and determination to this effort, the standards may have never become a reality.

Roger D. Fiske, Chairman
California Landscape Standards Committee

These standards were written as a reference for those involved in the California landscape construction industry. Presented in the sequence landscape construction operations are generally performed, the standards are divided into eight sections: General Requirements; Site Preparation-construction layout, clearing, grading, drainage, and sediment and erosion control; Hardscapes-wood, concrete, and masonry construction; Irrigation; Garden Lighting; Planting; Maintenance; and Interiorscaping.

Section I defines the general requirements or conditions which apply to all landscape construction operations. Sections 11 through VIII are written in the three-part format established by the Construction Specifications Institute. Part I describes the work included and general requirements specific to the section; Part 2 defines the acceptable products, i.e., materials, equipment, and fixtures to be incorporated into the work; and Part 3 defines procedures for the execution of the work.

All information is presented as it applies to specific landscape construction operations. The basic elements of a landscape have been included; however, the standards do not attempt to address all possibilities, nor are they intended to answer all questions. Throughout the text the word SHOULD, indicating the recommended MINIMUM, has been used in place of the word SHALL as used in specifications. As MINIMUM STANDARDS of acceptability, these standards are not intended to take the place of written specifications and are intended to be modified as deemed necessary for specific applications.

As a reference for the industry, as a guide for the landscape contractor, and as a learning tool for the student of landscape construction, it is hoped that the landscape standards serve their purpose well.

1.01 DESCRIPTION

1.02 GENERAL CONDITIONS
    A. SITE PROTECTION
    B. UNDERGROUND UTILITIES
    C. SAFETY
    D. EQUIPMENT
    E. SITE CLEANUP

1.03 QUALITY ASSURANCE
    A. REGULATORY REQUIREMENTS
        1. PERMITS
        2. CODES AND REGULATIONS
        3. CONTRACTORS LICENSE
        4. PEST CONTROL LICENSING
        5. SAFETY
    B. TESTING
    C. INSPECTIONS

1.04 REFERENCES

1.05 SUBMITTALS
    A. SHOP DRAWINGS
    B. SAMPLES
    C. PERMIT DOCUMENTS
    D. AS-BUILT DRAWINGS
    E. EQUIPMENT OPERATION MANUALS, MAINTENANCE
        INSTRUCTIONS, AND WARRANTIES

1.06 SITE CONDITIONS
    A. EXISTING CONDITIONS
        1. SITE INSPECTION
        2. UTILITIES
    B. ENVIRONMENTAL REQUIREMENTS

1.07 SCHEDULING

1.08 SUBSTITUTIONS

1.09 WARRANTY

1.01 DESCRIPTION

These general requirements provide specific conditions for all landscape operations. The conditions written in this section apply to all sections of the Landscape Standards, individually or combined.

1.02 GENERAL CONDITIONS

A. SITE PROTECTION

1. Contractor should protect and maintain all existing site improvements, structures, facilities, and utilities from damage, both above and below the ground.

2. Trees, shrubs, or other plant materials which are to remain on the site should be fully protected.

B. UNDERGROUND UTILITIES

1. Contractor MUST notify UNDERGROUND SERVICE ALERT at (800) 642-2444 at least 48 hours prior to commencing any underground excavations (grading, trenching, drilling, etc.) for location and marking of underground utilities to the meters.

2. Contractor should relocate or remove existing active utilities only as directed. Cost for relocation of utilities should be paid by the Owner. Where utilities are marked, careful hand excavation should be done to determine exact alignment and depth prior to starting excavations within marked areas.

C. SAFETY

1. Contractor should at all times exercise necessary precautions to provide for the protection of the public and employees.

2. Adequate barricades, flashers, fences, signs, and/or lights should be installed in all hazardous locations including, but not limited to, open excavations and areas of pedestrian and vehicular traffic.

3. All hazardous materials including, but not limited to, gasoline, solvents, and other similar materials should be stored in a safe and protected manner, according to all applicable regulations.

4. All stacked materials including lumber, pipe, and similar materials should be secured to prevent rolling or spilling.

D. EQUIPMENT

1. Contractor should provide and maintain all equipment necessary to perform the work.

2. Equipment should be safe, proper, efficient, and suited to, and for, the job. All equipment should be maintained in proper working condition.

3. Equipment must have all required safety devices in place and operational.

1.03 QUALITY ASSURANCE

A. REGULATORY REQUIREMENTS

1. PERMITS: It is the responsibility of the Contractor to obtain, and pay for, all permits required for the execution of the work.

2. CODES AND REGULATIONS: All work shall be performed in accordance with applicable laws, regulations, codes, and ordinances of state and local agencies.

3. CONTRACTORS LICENSE: Contractor must be properly and currently licensed by the California Contractors State License Board prior to entering into an agreement to perform work and may perform only such work as is within the scope of said license.

4. PEST CONTROL LICENSING: Contractor must be currently licensed by the California Department of Food and Agriculture and county registered to perform pest control work utilizing pesticides, herbicides, fungicides, or any other chemicals requiring licensing and registration.

5. SAFETY: Contractor shall comply with all applicable laws and regulations relating to safety, including the regulations of the California Division of Industrial Safety.

B. TESTING

1. If testing of any materials is required, such tests should be made by a qualified laboratory, staffed by personnel registered in the State of California. Cost of all testing shall be paid by the Owner, unless otherwise agreed upon.

2. Materials that fail to meet or exceed the specifications should be removed from the site and replaced with correct materials at the Contractor's expense.

C. INSPECTIONS

A schedule of inspections should be agreed upon between Contractor and Owner prior to commencement of work.

1.04 REFERENCES

AS REQUIRED

1.05 SUBMITTALS

A. SHOP DRAWINGS

If required, the Contractor should submit shop drawings (illustrations of methods of construction) prior to or during construction.

B. SAMPLES

Contractor should submit samples of materials to the Owner or Owner's representative, if required, prior to installation.

C. PERMIT DOCUMENTS

Upon final completion of work, the Contractor should provide to the Owner all approved stamped drawings and the signed-off permits required for the work.

D. AS-BUILT DRAWINGS

Upon final completion of the work, the Contractor should furnish the Owner with accurate, up-to-date drawings of any and all changes from the original plans made during the installation of all underground improvements.

E. EQUIPMENT OPERATION MANUALS, MAINTENANCE INSTRUCTIONS, AND WARRANTIES

Upon final completion of work, the Contractor should provide to the Owner written operation and maintenance instructions for all equipment installed on the site, along with manufacturer's warranties.

1.06 SITE CONDITIONS
A. EXISTING CONDITIONS
1. SITE INSPECTION
   a. Prior to commencement of work, the Contractor should be thoroughly familiar with any surveys and investigative reports directly related to the work to be performed. Owner is responsible to provide this information to the Contractor.
   b. Contractor should examine physical conditions at the site, document all conditions differing from those indicated in the contract documents, and notify the Owner or Owner's representative immediately.
   c. Underground obstructions such as, but not limited to, utilities, structures, water, rock, hard pan, or other obstructions which are not indicated on the plans or readily apparent at a site inspection, should be treated as additional work if encountered during construction.
2. UTILITIES
   a. Owner should provide the Contractor with accurate as-built plans or drawings of existing underground construction. The Contractor should not be held responsible for damages to underground utilities unless provided with accurate as-built drawings prior to the start of work.
   b. All water and utilities should be provided by the Owner, unless otherwise agreed upon.

B. ENVIRONMENTAL REQUIREMENTS
1. Contractor should be aware of, and adhere to, any regulations protecting special plants, wildlife, and natural environmental features that may be present on the site.
2. Contractor should be aware of any regulations put forth by the public authorities regarding dust and/or water pollution.

1.07 SCHEDULING

Scheduling of start and completion dates should be as agreed upon in writing by the Contractor and the Owner or Owner's representative.

1.08 SUBSTITUTIONS

Substitutions should be allowed only upon approval of the Owner or Owner's representative.

1.09 WARRANTY

A. Contractor should be responsible for defective materials and faulty workmanship while the work is in progress. Upon relinquishing care, custody, and control of a project, the Contractor should be responsible for defective materials and faulty workmanship for a minimum period of 90 days for plant materials and one year for all other work.

B. Any damages to site improvements and facilities caused by the Contractor's neglect should be corrected and paid for by the Contractor at no cost to the Owner.

C. After relinquishing care, custody, and control of a project, the Contractor should not be held responsible for the results of improper maintenance or neglect.

D. At no time should the Contractor be responsible for damages due to vandalism, civil disorder, floods, earthquakes, or other events beyond the Contractor's control.

PART 1 – GENERAL
      1.01   DESCRIPTION
      1.02   WORK INCLUDED
      1.03   CONTRACTOR RESPONSIBILITY

PART 2 – PRODUCTS
      2.01   STAKES
      2.02   FLAGS
      2.03   LABELS

PART 3 – EXECUTION

1.01 DESCRIPTION

Construction layout establishes the detailed location of each element of a landscape project.

1.02 WORK INCLUDED

This section includes the accurate measurement, layout, and staking – both horizontal and vertical - of each landscape element on the drawings as required for clearing, grading, drainage, hardscapes, irrigation, lighting, and planting operations.

The provisions of SECTION I - GENERAL REQUIREMENTS apply to the work under this Section as though written herein in full.

1.03 CONTRACTOR RESPONSIBILITY

A. Unless otherwise provided, all work should be laid out on the premises by the Contractor, who should be held responsible for its correctness.

B. Contractor should be responsible for the use of all survey information furnished by the Owner and should cross-check line and grade from adjacent bench marks or staking to determine that existing survey staking or bench marks have not been accidentally displaced.

C. Contractor should preserve all bench marks, survey control points, reference points, and any other permanent points. Any reference points damaged by the Contractor's operations should be properly replaced at the Contractor's expense.

D. Construction survey stakes which are damaged or destroyed by the Contractor's operations should be restored in proper position at the Contractor's expense.

2.01 **STAKES**

Stakes should be of wood or metal and of such length as to be clearly visible.

2.02 **FLAGS**

Flags should be brightly colored cloth or plastic and substantial enough to withstand the natural elements during the construction period.

2.03 **LABELS**

Labels should be bright bands of such length to encircle branches of trees and shrubs, and other landscape elements marked for protection.

Contractor should accurately lay out and stake each element shown on the landscape plans prior to commencing work and/or as necessary during construction to accurately assure the proper finish elevation and location of all elements included in the project.

PART 1 – GENERAL

PART 2 – PRODUCTS

PART 3 – EXECUTION

1.01 DESCRIPTION

Clearing provides for the proper removal and disposal of designated site improvements, vegetation, and debris prior to commencement of other construction operations.

1.02 WORK INCLUDED

This section includes the protection of all site improvements and plant materials to be retained, installation of necessary protective fencing, and removal of specified structures, paving and other existing improvements, plant material, and debris.

The provisions of SECTION 1- GENERAL REQUIREMENTS apply to the work under this section as though written herein in full.

1.03 REFERENCES

CALTRANS STANDARD SPECIFICATIONS, Current Edition

1.04 EXISTING CONDITIONS

Prior to the clearing operations, the Contractor should meet with the Owner or Owner's representative to designate all trees and shrubs to remain on the site and those to be removed. No trees should be removed without prior approval. Where possible, existing trees should be retained.

PART 2 — PRODUCTS

2.01 PROTECTIVE FENCING OR BARRIERS

Protective fencing or barriers should be wire or plastic mesh, solid lumber, or similar material at least 36 inches high.

PART 3 — EXECUTION

3.01 EXISTING SITE IMPROVEMENTS

Existing site improvements which are to remain should be protected with appropriate fencing, staking, or flags.

3.02 TREE AND SHRUB PROTECTION

A. Individual trees which are to remain should be protected with the placement of an approved barrier at the drip-line of the tree.

B. Groups of trees or shrubs which are to remain should be protected with approved barriers firmly anchored to the ground at an adequate distance to protect the planting.

C. No material should be stockpiled; no equipment parked, repaired, or refueled; and no oil, gasoline, paint, or other contaminants dumped or stored within 25 feet of the drip-line of trees and shrubs which are to remain.

D. All plant material to remain on the site should be inspected by a qualified person for disease and pest damage, and appropriate recommendations for necessary treatment should be made to the Owner.

3.03 MOVING EXISTING TREES

Tree moving or relocation should be done by an approved arborist or experienced contractor.

3.04 CLEARING AND GRUBBING

A. Clearing and grubbing operations should begin only after protective fencing and barriers have been installed. Protective measures should be maintained throughout the duration of the project.

B. No grade changes should be made that will affect the root systems of existing trees and shrubs which are to remain.

C. All stumps, roots, and debris should be removed in areas of excavations.

D. All debris should be removed in areas of fill. Where fills are less than three feet deep, all stumps and root systems should be removed. Where fills are greater than three feet deep, stumps and roots should be cut level with original grade.

E. In areas of no grade changes, all stumps and roots should be dug or cut out to a depth of 18 inches. Surface vegetation, debris, and rocks larger than two inches in diameter should be removed to establish a clean surface. Stumps and large roots may be ground with a stump grinding machine.

F. In areas where drainage systems are to be installed, all stumps and roots should be removed. The use of heavy equipment in their removal should be minimized to avoid excessive compaction.

G. All stump and root holes should be filled with suitable material, in accordance with fill and compaction requirements.

H. All noxious weeds and unwanted vegetation should be eradicated by approved methods.

3.05 DISPOSAL

All cleared site improvements, trees, stumps, roots, brush, vegetation, and debris should be removed from the site and disposed of in a legal manner. Burning on-site should not be allowed.

PART 1 – GENERAL

PART 2 – PRODUCTS

PART 3 – EXECUTION

1.01 DESCRIPTION

Grading involves changing the existing elevations of a site to provide surface drainage and allow for the construction and installation of landscape improvements.

1.02 WORK INCLUDED

This section includes rough grading, import and export of soils, excavation and embankment fills, compacting, topsoil placement, finish grading, and other related work.

The provisions of SECTION 1- GENERAL REQUIREMENTS apply to the work under this section as though written herein in full.

1.03 QUALITY ASSURANCE

When required, testing of compacted fill and import soil should be done by a certified testing laboratory.

1.04 REFERENCES

CALTRANS STANDARD SPECIFICATIONS, Current Edition

1.05 SITE CONDITIONS
A. EXISTING CONDITIONS

1. Prior to commencement of grading operations, the Contractor should be aware of any and all hazards the grading operation may create for pedestrian or vehicular traffic and implement proper precautionary measures.

2. Existing structures, pavements, curbs and gutters, conduits, fences and walls, and other facilities - both above and below ground - should be properly protected and maintained in a satisfactory manner. Contractor should repair and restore damages caused by neglect or construction operations at the Contractor's own expense.

B. ENVIRONMENTAL CONDITIONS

Contractor should be responsible for dust control during all grading operations, as required for health and safety. Wherever practical, water spray should be used to keep dust to a minimum.

1.06 CONTRACTOR RESPONSIBILITY

A. Any damage, such as compaction or rutting, caused to existing grades on the site during the grading operations should be repaired, and the damaged areas returned to their original grade and state of permeability.

B. Settlement or erosion that occurs during the grading operations should be repaired, and grades reestablished to the required elevations and slopes.

2.01   FILL SOIL MATERIAL

A.   Fill soil should be of comparable composition as existing soil on the site and should be free of rocks larger than three inches in diameter, vegetation, and other debris.

B.   Where excavation areas yield material that is predominately rock or gravel, such material may be used as fill only in areas where it will be buried three or more feet deep. Under no circumstances should such material be used any closer to the surface, except with the approval of the Owner or Owner's representative.

C.   An on-site source of any additional soil required to balance the grading requirements may, when appropriate, be designated by the Owner or Owner's representative.

D.   All imported soil should be free of diseases, pests, and noxious weeds.

2.02   TOPSOIL

All imported topsoil should be natural soil, graded to not larger than 3/4 inch, and should be free of animal or vegetable matter, diseases, pests, and noxious weeds.

3.01   SLOPE RATIOS

The maximum slope ratio should be not more than three feet horizontal to one foot vertical, unless otherwise approved by the Owner or Owner's representative and/or the grading inspector.

3.02   ROUGH GRADING

A.   **GRADE TOLERANCES**

All rough grading should be accurate to within two-tenths (0.2) foot of designed elevation. Pockets or depressions which will not readily drain should not be allowed to remain.

B.   All grades should be prepared with a smooth, natural appearance, blending into the adjacent areas. Rough-graded areas should be free of large clods of dirt, rocks, sharp rises, unnatural mounds or ridges, and debris or foreign material.

3.03   FILL AND COMPACTION

A.   All vegetative matter should be removed from the surface where any fill is to be placed, and the surface ripped or scarified to the depth specified and until the surface is free from ruts, hummocks, or other uneven features which would prevent uniform compaction.

B.   Where fills are made on hillsides or slopes, the slope of the existing soil where fill is to be placed should be ripped or scarified to a depth of at least eight inches.

C. Where fill soil is to be placed on a slope with a slope ratio greater than six feet horizontal to one foot vertical, a licensed engineer should be employed to design appropriate methods of fill retention.

D. Fill soil should be placed in layers which, when compacted, will not exceed eight inches in depth. The first layer should be spread evenly and incorporated into the existing soil to an adequate depth to ensure uniform compaction.

E. Cut and fill areas should be kept shaped and drained during construction. Swales and drainage ways should be maintained in such a manner as to drain effectively at all times. Graded areas should be protected against the elements until completion and acceptance of the work.

F. Compaction should be accomplished while the fill material has a moisture content sufficient to allow the necessary compaction to be obtained. Soil compaction should not be done when it is raining or when the soil contains excessive moisture.

G. Minimum degrees of compaction should be achieved to meet the following requirements:

> Top one foot beneath walks or paving ....95% relative density
> Other fill beneath walks or paving..........90% relative density
> Fill in planting areas ....80% relative density
> Other non-structural fill or backfill ....85% relative density

3.04 TOPSOIL PLACEMENT

Placement of imported topsoil, if required, should be done prior to finish grading.

3.05 FINISH GRADING

Finish graded surfaces should be smooth, uniform, and totally free of debris, and rocks and soil lumps larger than one inch. All grades should blend into the adjacent areas in a smooth and natural appearance. Finish grades abutting walks, drives, or structures should be even and uniform. All finish grades should slope away from improvements at a minimum 2% gradient.

PART 1 – GENERAL

PART 2 – PRODUCTS

PART 3 – EXECUTION

1.01 DESCRIPTION

Drainage systems control water movement within a site. These systems provide for the safety and convenience of occupants and the protection of structures, other improvements, and usable lot areas from water damage by the collection and disposal of surface and sub-surface water.

1.02 WORK INCLUDED

This section includes the installation of surface and sub-surface systems, drainage structures, and other related work.

The provisions of SECTION 1 - GENERAL REQUIREMENTS apply to the work under this section as though written herein in full.

1.03 QUALITY ASSURANCE PER LOCAL CONTROL AGENCIES

1.04 REFERENCES

AMERICAN SOCIETY FOR TESTING AND MATERIALS bulletins CALTRANS STANDARD SPECIFICATIONS, Current Edition

1.05 SUBMITTALS

Shop drawings may be required for drainage structures.

1.06 EXISTING CONDITIONS

Existing structures, pavements, curbs and gutters, conduits, fences and walls, and other facilities - both above and below grade - should be properly protected and maintained in a satisfactory manner. Contractor should repair and restore damages caused by neglect or construction operations at the Contractor's own expense.

2.01 GENERAL

All pipe, pipe fittings, accessories, and appurtenances should be new and of the types, sizes, and materials as required.

2.02 DRAINAGE PIPE

A. Drainage pipe should be of any material listed by its ASTM number as being suitable for drainage application. All Pipe and/or fittings for such application should be furnished with product data from a nationally recognized standards or building code organization which states that the pipe is suitable for the purpose intended.

B. Types of drainage pipe include, but are not limited to, clay, plastic, steel, cast iron, ductile iron, corrugated metal, reinforced concrete, non-reinforced concrete, and fiberglass reinforced plastic pipe.

C. All fittings should be of identical or compatible material

3.01 MATERIAL STORAGE

All pipe and pipe fittings should be stored and handled in a manner that will prevent damage to the pipe and joining faces, and should be protected from unnecessary exposure to the sun's rays. All pipe stored in piles should be adequately supported to prevent distortion, and other material should not be stored on top of the pipe.

3.02 GENERAL INSTALLATION REQUIREMENTS

A. Temporary protection should be provided by barricading all open excavations and work areas. Barricades should be equipped with warning lights operating from dusk to daylight.

B. No pipe should be installed until it has been determined that all pipe, from one point of connection to another point, can be installed at the location and slope indicated.

C. All lines should be laid true to line and grade. Sections of pipe should be laid and fitted together so that, when completed, the pipe will have a smooth and uniform flow line.

D. Trench bottoms and bedding should be shaped and compacted as required to give substantial uniform circumferential support to the lower fourth of the pipe circumference the full length of each pipe.

E. All open ends of pipe should be fully protected, to prevent earth or other substances from entering the pipe during the construction period. As the work progresses, interiors of pipe and fittings should be carefully cleaned of all dirt, grease, cement, or foreign matter of every description.

3.03 SURFACE DRAINAGE

A. SYSTEM DESCRIPTION

Surface drainage systems use the contouring of the ground to direct the flow of water as sheet drainage or into swales.

B. Provisions should be made for the best available routing of surface water, to assure that buildings or other site improvements are not endangered by runoff.

C. Drainage swales should not carry runoff across walks in quantities that will make the walks unfit for use. Walks should not be used as drainage swales.

1. Drainage swales should receive a protective lining as required and wherever concentration of runoff could cause erosion.

2. Swales in lawn areas should be graded at a minimum 2% slope.

3.04   SUB-SURFACE DRAINAGE

A.   SYSTEM DESCRIPTION

Sub-surface drainage systems include the use of gravel-filled trenches, which may or may not contain perforated pipe, to intercept, collect, and direct sub-surface water flow.

B.   French drains should be dug with a bottom slope of 1% minimum and should be limited to not more than 50 feet in length. A perforated drain pipe may be installed at the bottom of the French drain.

C.   Pipe should be joined above ground or in place, in accordance with the manufacturer's recommendations for the specific type of pipe used. Pipe and fittings should not be moved after joining, until properly cooled or cured and in accordance with the pipe manufacturer's tables for time delay between joining and use.

D.   Pipe should be laid with a minimum 1% slope, unless indicated otherwise.

E.   Clean, graded, washed drain rock should be installed around the pipe. Positive protection should be provided over drain rock during backfill to prevent contamination of the drain rock with soil. Approved soil filter fabric should be used to envelop the drain rock.

F.   Perforated pipe should be laid with perforations down.

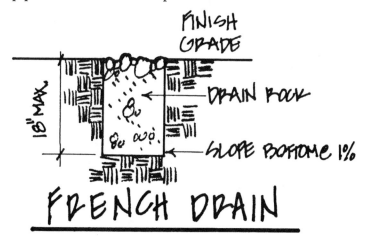

FINISH GRADE

18" MAX

DRAIN ROCK

SLOPE BOTTOM @ 1%

FRENCH DRAIN

FINISH GRADE

SOIL COVER

FILTER FABRIC

DRAIN ROCK

PERFORATED PIPE @ 1% SLOPE

SUB-SURFACE DRAIN

26

3.05 UNDERGROUND STORM DRAIN SYSTEMS

A. SYSTEM DESCRIPTION

Underground storm drainage systems consist of inlets or basins which collect surface drainage in a pipe system for discharge into an appropriate outlet.

B. Installations of storm drains within public right-of-ways must be accomplished in accordance with agency standards for work within its jurisdiction.

C. Connections of storm sewers to existing city or district storm sewers must be accomplished in accordance with the conditions of the permits for such connections.

3.06 INLET STRUCTURES

A. DESCRIPTION

Inlet structures include drain inlets, drop inlets and catch basins, clean-outs, and other entrance connections or discharge components of a site drainage system.

B. Drainage structures should be installed in sizes and shapes as required. They should be precast concrete, poured-in-place concrete, constructed from concrete masonry units or common brick, or premolded plastic. Poured-in-place concrete should be reinforced as detailed. Concrete masonry unit or brick structures should be reinforced where walls are greater than 24 inches high.

3.07 FINAL GRADING AND TESTING

A. The final grade adjacent to drainage structures should be adjusted to provide positive slopes and drainage into inlet structures without standing water.

B. Upon completion of a drainage system, all pipes and drainage structures should be flushed to ensure there is no build-up of dirt and/or debris, and check for positive flow of water to the point of discharge.

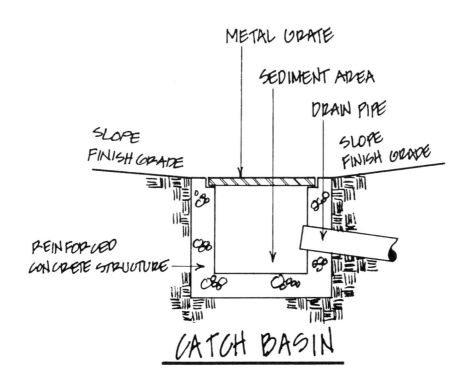

CATCH BASIN

PART 1 – GENERAL

PART 2 – PRODUCTS

PART 3 – EXECUTION

1.01 DESCRIPTION

Sediment and erosion control provides control of water runoff, and short- and long-term protection from erosion as a result of construction operations.

1.02 WORK INCLUDED

This section includes the protection of native vegetation, installation of sedimentation controls, control of slope construction, stabilization of slope surfaces, control of runoff, protection of watercourses, disposal of excavated materials, and planting of exposed soils.

The provisions of SECTION 1- GENERAL REQUIREMENTS apply to the work under this section as though written herein in full.

1.03 QUALITY ASSURANCE PER LOCAL CONTROL AGENCIES

1.04 REFERENCES

CALIFORNIA FOOD AND AGRICULTURE CODE CALTRANS STANDARD SPECIFICATIONS, Current Edition

2.01 SEDIMENT AND EROSION CONTROL DEVICES
AS SPECIFIED

2.02 MULCH

A. Choice of mulch should be based on the following or as specified:

1. Effectiveness of materials

2. Size of area

3. Steepness of slope

4. Soil depth and surface hardness

5. Wind conditions

6. Availability of materials

7. Access to roadway and slope orientation (uphill or downhill)

8. Fire hazard, weed growth, and maintenance considerations

B. Commonly used mulches include straw, wood fiber, wood chips or bark, and fabric or mats.

2.03 SEED

A. Choice of seed should be based on the following or as specified:

1. Rapid germination and growth

2. Fibrous root mat

3. Availability

4. Fire hazard considerations

5. Fertilizer requirements

B. All seeds should be labeled in accordance with the California Food and Agriculture Code.

C. A density of 160 viable seed per square foot for broadcast type seeding is recommended in California.

D. The rate of seed application may be adjusted according to erosion hazard or as specified.

2.04 FERTILIZER

All fertilizers must conform to the requirements of the California Food and Agriculture Code and should be used in accordance with manufacturer's recommended application rates.

PART 3 — EXECUTION

3.01 NATIVE VEGETATION

A. Native vegetation should be retained, protected, and supplemented, wherever possible. When vegetation must be removed, the method should be one that will minimize the erosive effects from the removal. Exposure of soil to erosion by removing vegetation should be limited to the area required for immediate construction operations.

B. In no event should the native vegetative ground cover be destroyed, removed, or disturbed more than 15 days prior to grading, unless otherwise approved by the engineer representing the permit issuing authority.

3.02 GRADING PRACTICES

A. All land within a development should be graded to drain and dispose of surface water without ponding, except where approved by the permit issuring authority.

B. Grading operations should be conducted so as to prevent damaging effects of sediment production and dust on the site and on adjoining properties.

C. In order to prevent polluting discharges from occurring, erosion and sediment control devices should be employed for all grading and filling. Control devices and measures which may be required include, but are not limited to, the following:

1. Energy-absorbing devices to reduce the velocity of runoff water.

2. Sedimentation controls, such as sediment debris basins and sediment traps. Any trapped sediment should be removed to a disposal site as it accumulates.

3. Dispersal of water runoff from developed areas over large, undisturbed areas.

4. Multiple discharge points to reduce the volume of runoff over localized areas.

3.03 SLOPE CONSTRUCTION

A. Slopes, both cut and fill, should not be steeper than three to one, unless a thorough geological and engineering analysis indicates that steeper slopes are safe and erosion control measures are specified.

B. Slopes should not be constructed so as to endanger or disturb adjoining property.

3.04 SLOPE SURFACE STABILIZATION

A. Temporary mulching, seeding, or other suitable stabilization measures should be used to protect exposed critical areas during construction.

B. Ditches or dikes should be installed at the top of cut or fill slopes where surface runoff could flow down the slopes.

3.05 SEDIMENT CONTROL

A. Sediment should be retained on the site.

B. Sediment basins, sediment traps, or similar sediment control measures should be installed before extensive clearing and grading operations begin.

C. Any trapped sediment that accumulates during construction should be removed to a disposal site.

3.06 CONTROL OF RUNOFF

A. Provisions should be made to control the increased runoff caused by changed and surface soil conditions during and after development.

B. To prevent excess runoff, the rate of surface water runoff should be structurally retarded.

C. When making surface changes:

1. Collect on-site surface runoff and dispose of it at non-erosive velocities to the point of discharge into the common watercourse of the drainage area.

2. Direct existing and potential off-site runoff water into sediment basins, silt traps, or similar measure.

3. Retain sediment being transported by runoff water on-site through the use of sediment basins, silt traps, or similar measure.

D. Concentration of surface water should be permitted only in protected swales or watercourses.

E. Where drainage swales are used to divert surface waters, they should be vegetated or otherwise protected from scour.

3.07 PROTECTION OF WATERCOURSES

A. Fills should not encroach on natural watercourses or constructed channels.

B. Fills placed adjacent to watercourses should have suitable protection against erosion during flooding.

C. Grading equipment should not cross or disturb live stream channels without adequate temporary facilities which will prevent sediment pollution.

D. Excavated material should not be deposited or stored in or alongside watercourses where the materials can be washed away by high water or storm runoff.

3.08 DISPOSAL OF CLEARED VEGETATION

Vegetation removed during the clearing operations should be disposed of as follows:

A. All or some of the cleared vegetation may be chipped, if appropriate, for use as mulch or compost on the site.

B. All other material should be disposed of in a manner and at a location approved by the local authorities.

3.09 STOCKPILING OF EXCAVATED SOIL

A. All or some of the topsoil on the site may be stockpiled for use on areas of revegetation.

B. Stockpiled soil should be located so it cannot become a source of off-site sediment damage if erosion occurs and far enough from streams or drainage ways so that surface runoff cannot carry sediment downstream.

C. Material from trenches and pits should be stockpiled on the up slope side of excavations. Trenches and pits should be promptly backfilled and compacted to reduce the risk of erosion.

D. Mulch or other protective coverings should be applied on stockpiled material which will be exposed through the winter season or will face a high risk of summer rains.

3.10 TIMING FOR PLANTING EXPOSED SOILS

Seeds should be planted in time for the first germination causing rains. Most California locations require this to be before October 31st.

A. If seeding is done long before the rainy season, loss caused by birds and insects may be significant.

B. Seeds should be planted while temperatures are mild and daylight is relatively long (before the end of November) so plants can establish top growth and establish a root mat capable of resisting the erosive force of major storms by 30 days after the first rain.

C. Irrigation is expensive and not necessary, unless the area is particularly critical. Once begun, it must be continued until plant cover is fully matured. Ceasing irrigation after germination will result in seedlings being killed by drought before producing seeds.

3.11 PLANTING EXPOSED SOILS

A. The surface to be seeded should be rough and broken up so that it can hold seeds and retard runoff. As an area is graded, it should not be smoothed to a hard, slick surface by grading equipment, but left in a rough or serrated condition.

B. Whenever slope, soil, or timing factors allow, the seeds should be covered with soil or mulch.

C. Small areas can be hand-seeded to provide uniform coverage. A seed drill works well on level areas, but should not be used on slopes greater than three to one. When seeds are drilled, seed and fertilizer quantities may be reduced compared to broadcast application.

D. Hydroseeding/hydromulching is most efficient for seeding slopes steeper than three to one. The advantage of hydroseeding/hydromulching is the ability of seeds and mulch material to adhere to steep topography.

E. Application of mulch increases plant establishment and protects a disturbed site from erosive forces. Mulch holds fertilizers, seeds, and soil in place in the presence of wind, rain, and runoff and maintains moisture near the soil surface.

F. Straw is acceptable mulch material under the following conditions:

1. Open areas accessible by straw blowing equipment within 50 feet

2. Slopes flatter than 1-1/2 to 1

3. Fill slopes

4. Non-windy areas

5. Downhill or downwind applications

6. Hand-spread in very small locations

G. Hydromulching is preferred under the following conditions:

1. Areas far from road access that can be reached with hoses

2. Slopes steeper than three to one

3. Slopes with shallow soil covers

4. Windy areas

5. Where fire hazard or weed growth is undesirable

PART 1 – GENERAL

1.01	DESCRIPTION
1.02	WORK INCLUDED
1.03	QUALITY ASSURANCE
1.04	REFERENCES
1.05	SCHEDULING

PART 2 – PRODUCTS

2.01	LUMBER
2.02	OTHER MATERIALS

PART 3 – EXECUTION

3.01	LAYOUT
3.02	LUMBER STORAGE
3.03	GENERAL CONSTRUCTION REQUIREMENTS
3.04	FENCE CONSTRUCTION
3.05	WOOD DECK CONSTRUCTION
3.06	WOOD GARDEN STAIRS
3.07	BENCHES
3.08	ARBORS
3.09	WOOD RETAINING WALLS
3.10	PLANTER BOXES
3.11	HEADER BOARDS

1.01 DESCRIPTION

Wood construction provides both functional and esthetic elements in the landscape.

1.02 WORK INCLUDED

This section includes the construction of fences, decks, garden stairs, benches, arbors, retaining walls, planter boxes, and header boards.

The provisions of SECTION 1- GENERAL REQUIREMENTS apply to the work under this section as though written herein in full.

1.03 QUALITY ASSURANCE

Permits, when required, must be secured prior to commencement of construction.

1.04 REFERENCES

CALIFORNIA REDWOOD ASSOCIATION publications
HOW TO DESIGN & BUILD DECKS & PATIOS
UNIFORM BUILDING CODE, Current Edition
WESTERN WOOD PRESERVERS INSTITUTE publications
WESTERN WOOD PRODUCTS ASSOCIATION publications

1.05 SCHEDULING

All grading and underground utilities which relate to work in this section should be completed prior to commencement of wood construction.

2.01 LUMBER

  A. REDWOOD

Dimensional stability, strength and durability, and special beauty make redwood one of the most widely used and most suitable materials for outdoor wood construction. Redwood is available in a variety of grades, grain patterns, seasonings, and textures.

1. GRADES: All redwood grades should comply with the grading accepted by the California Redwood Association. Different redwood lumber grade names may be used; however, the following grades are universally recognized:

  a. Architectural Grades: Clear All Heart, all heartwood with the graded face free of knots; Clear, includes sapwood in varying amounts and may have one or two small, tight knots on the graded face; B Grade, contains limited knots and sapwood.

  b. Garden Grades: Construction Heart, all heartwood with knots; Construction Common, includes sapwood and knots; Merchantable Heart, heartwood with larger knots; Merchantable, contains streaks of sapwood, larger knots, and some holes.

c. Other Grades: Select Heart, all heartwood with knots slightly smaller than construction heart; Select, contains sapwood with knots slightly smaller than construction common.

2. GRAIN PATTERNS: Redwood lumber is available in either vertical or flat grain patterns. Garden grades come in mixed grains. Vertical grain should be used where a smoother surface is desirable.

3. SEASONINGS: Most redwood is available either unseasoned ("green") or airdried. Architectural grades of redwood can be ordered "Certified Kiln Dried" for applications requiring minimal shrinkage.

4. TEXTURE: Redwood is available in surfaced (smooth), rough surfaced (rough), or rehewn (slightly rough) which provides a special rough-textured, decorative face.

   a. The finish of surfaced lumber emphasizes the grain and color of the wood. Surfaced redwood is recommended for deck, bench, and other surfaces which will be touched or painted.

   b. Rough surfaced redwood is appropriate for many uses in landscape construction and has excellent retention of penetrating natural oils and sealers, and stain finishes.

   c. Rehewn redwood is used when the special effects of this lumber treatment are desirable.

5. GROUND CONTACT: All redwood used in ground contact or within 12 inches of the ground must be all heart redwood.

B. PRESSURE TREATED LUMBER

1. DESCRIPTION: Lumber that has been pressure treated with wood preservatives which inhibit insect and fungi damage. Various types of treatment are utilized to preserve lumber for construction use, including above ground, ground contact, freshwater, or saltwater application.

2. USES: Pressure treated lumber is used wherever wood is to be placed in or within 12 inches of the ground or in water, in contact with masonry, or when exposed to wet or damp environments.

3. LABELING: All pressure treated lumber should bear the American Wood Preservers Bureau AWPB stamp.

   a. Ground Contact: All wood treated for ground contact will be marked For Ground Contact and will bear a designation such as "LP-22", which means it was treated with a waterborne preservative for ground contact or freshwater submersion.

   b. Above Ground Use: An "LP-2" designation indicates the wood was treated for above ground use only.

   c. Designations: Letters other than "LP" indicate that the wood was treated with other chemicals. Single digits are used for above ground use treatments; double digits are used for ground contact or freshwater use treatments.

C. OTHER LUMBER

All other lumber used for permanent landscape construction should be Douglas fir or western red cedar of an appropriate grade for the specific usage as recommended by the Western Wood Products Association or comparable grading bureau.

D. QUALITY

All lumber should be clean, of standard sizes as required, and free of splits, shakes, wane, or other defects.

E. SUBSTITUTIONS

No substitutions are acceptable for all heart redwood or pressure treated lumber when used in a ground contact or within 12 inches of the ground.

2.02 OTHER MATERIALS

A. FASTENERS

All exposed nails, screws, hinges, latches, or other fasteners should be galvanized or non-corrosive metal, sized as required.

B. CONNECTORS

Non-corrosive connectors should be used for beams, joists, rafters, and posts, sized as required.

C. WOOD FINISHES

1. PROTECTION: All lumber used in wood construction should be protected from the elements to prevent the wood from excessive cupping, checking, and splitting.

2. TYPES: Wood finish products include water repellents, water- or oil-based stains and paints and specific wood preservatives.

3. SELECTION: The choice of wood finish products will depend on the degree of durability and the appearance desired. All wood finishes should be chosen based on manufacturer's recommendations for the specific application.

D. CONCRETE

All concrete used for the installation of piers, footings, or below grade posts should be a minimum of 5-sack mix.

E. PIER BLOCKS

Manufactured pre-cast concrete blocks with a redwood block cast into the top of the block for attachment of a post. Pier blocks should be set on top of a concrete footing a minimum of six inches above the ground, to provide protection to the posts and beams.

F. FLASHING

Non-corrosive flat metal used to provide termite protection to a building where wood structures, such as fences or decks that are in ground contact, are attached to a building or similar structure.

3.01 LAYOUT

The exact location of each wood construction element should be accurately established and marked on the site prior to commencing work, to assure proper alignment of all constructed elements.

3.02 LUMBER STORAGE

Lumber stored at the job site should be protected from sun, rain, or other adverse weather conditions. The lumber should be stacked flat and kept off the ground at least six inches. Care should be taken when storing redwood on or near concrete paving; staining can occur if the wood becomes wet.

3.03 GENERAL CONSTRUCTION REQUIREMENTS

A. Joints should be accurately made and securely nailed. Nails should not be driven close to ends of lumber where splitting may occur. Any boards or timbers split by fasteners during construction should be replaced.

B. Splices in beams, rails, or similar units should not be allowed except on top of a supporting member.

C. All posts embedded below grade must be all heart redwood or pressure treated lumber rated for ground contact.

D. All wood surfaces should be sealed with an appropriate wood finish product, applied per the manufacturer's recommendations, to adequately protect the lumber from splitting or checking.

3.04 FENCE CONSTRUCTION
A. GRADES OF LUMBER

1. Posts must be all-heart redwood or pressure treated lumber rated for ground contact.

2. Rails should be all-heart redwood.

3. Boards should be a nominal minimum thickness of 1 inch. The actual dimension should be not less than 3/4 inch. Boards can be surfaced or rough.

B. LOCATION

Care should be taken when laying out a fence on or near a property line. If a fence is constructed on the property line, it becomes a "community" fence and belongs to both property owners.

C. HEIGHT

The height of fences and screens can vary according to application, location, and local building code restrictions. The most commonly constructed property line fence is six feet in height.

D. POST INSTALLATION

1. SIZE OF POST: The length and dimension will vary depending on the height of the fence. The typical six-foot fence should be constructed using 8-foot long 4x4 posts.

2. SPACING: Posts should be spaced no farther than eight feet on center.

3. HOLE SIZE: The size will vary, depending on the height and dimensions of the post. Post holes for the typical six-foot fence should be a minimum of 12 inches diameter by 24 inches deep.

4. POST ALIGNMENT: All posts should be installed true to horizontal and vertical alignment.

5. SETTING

   a. Posts should be set in 5-sack wet concrete mix with 3/4-inch aggregate or 6-sack wet concrete mix with 3/8-inch aggregate.

   b. The concrete should encircle the post full depth of the hole to above grade, to allow water to drain away from the post.

   c. The bottom of the post should not be encased in concrete.

6. TERMITE PROTECTION: Metal flashing should be installed between posts and buildings or other structures.

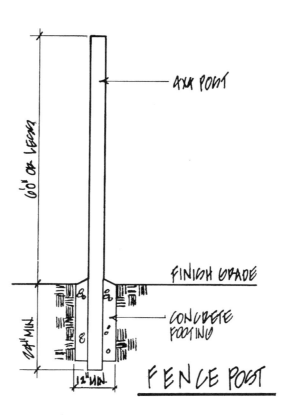

E. RAILS AND BOARDS INSTALLATION

1. RAILS: Should be evenly spaced on the posts, either level or parallel to the ground, and securely fastened with appropriate fasteners. The bottom rail should be a minimum of six inches above finish grade.

2. BOARDS: Should be positioned on the rails with edges plumb and tops level, and secured with appropriate fasteners.

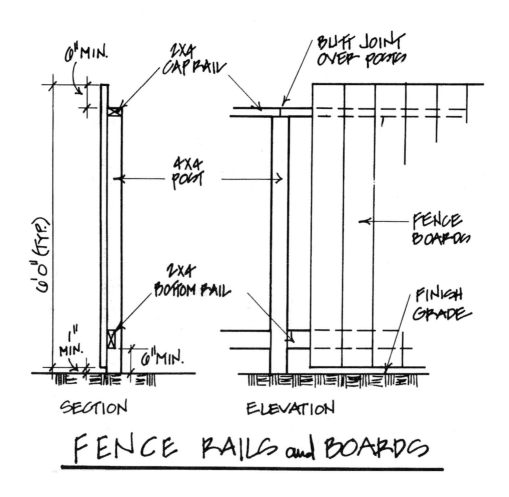

FENCE RAILS and BOARDS

F.   GATE CONSTRUCTION

Wood gates should be structurally sound, functional for the intended use, and constructed to match or be compatible with the adjacent fence or structure.

1. POSTS: Gate posts must be all heart redwood or pressure treated lumber rated for ground contact. The dimensions of posts can vary, depending on the design of the gate. Posts must have the strength to support the weight of the gate and resist stress when the gate is opened and closed. Posts should be set vertical and parallel in the same manner as fence posts.

2. FRAME: Gate frames should be constructed with butt joints, using 2x4 all heart redwood minimum. The corner joints should be reinforced with wood gussets or metal braces. To eliminate sag when the gate is hung, a diagonal wood brace should be installed between the top inside corner on the latch side and the bottom inside corner on the hinge side. A tension cable may be used as an alternative, and should be attached to the opposite corners of the gate frame.

3. BOARDS: Face boards should be secured to the frame with appropriate fasteners.

4. HANGING: Gate frame should be securely attached to the gate posts with 4-inch hinges. A minimum of three hinges should be used to properly support a five- to six-foot height gate.

5. LATCH: A substantial latch should be installed with appropriate fasteners to securely hold the gate closed.

6. GATE STOPS: Most gate latches are not designed to act as a gate stop. To prevent the destruction of the latch, appropriate gate stops should be installed.

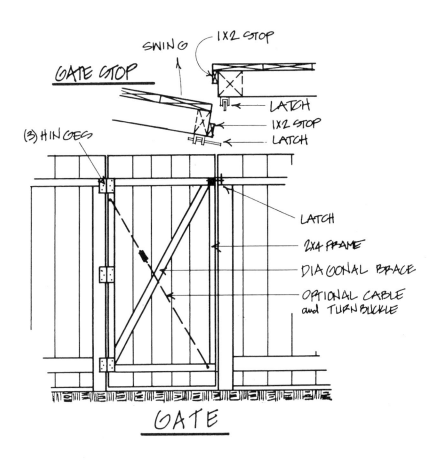

3.05 WOOD DECK CONSTRUCTION

A. GRADES OF LUMBER

Various species of wood can be used in deck construction. The understructure of a deck is typically constructed from redwood. All lumber, including pier posts, beams and joists, within 12 inches of the ground must be all heart redwood or pressure treated lumber rated for ground contact. Redwood is the most commonly used wood for deck boards, stairs, and facia trim. Exposed surfaces should be surfaced lumber of chosen grade.

B. STRUCTURAL DESIGN

A building permit is required in most areas for decks constructed more than 30 inches above the ground. A licensed engineer may be required to design the structural portion of the deck.

REFER TO APPENDIX POST, BEAM AND JOIST SIZING AND SPACING CHARTS

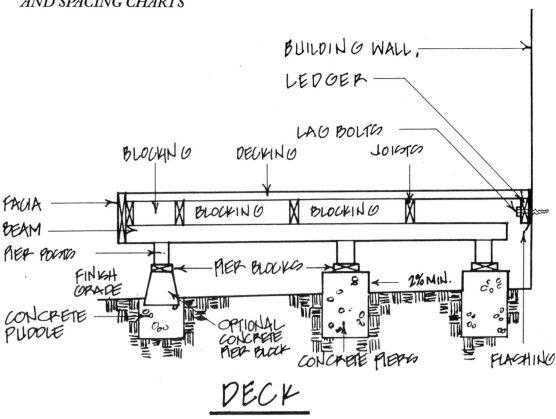

DECK

C. PIERS

1. LAYOUT: Support piers should be laid out to provide proper and adequate support for the deck structure, with correct spacing and alignment for the deck design. Pier spacing should be a maximum of four feet for 4x4 beams and six feet for 4x6 beams on edge.

2. PIER SUPPORT: Deck design, soil type, and local codes will determine the necessary type of pier construction. Pier holes should be a minimum of 12 inches in diameter by 12 inches deep and filled with wet concrete mix. If pier blocks are to be used, a standard concrete pier block should be set on the wet concrete true to line and level. The top of the pier block should be a minimum of six inches above grade, to allow for proper clearance between wood and soil.

42

3. DRAINAGE: The soil excavated from the pier holes should be removed from the area or spread out evenly so as not to interfere with proper and adequate drainage under the deck. The area must be graded to allow water to drain away from the deck area or into a designed drainage system.

4. PIER POSTS: All heart redwood, adequately sized to support the deck structure, should be used for pier posts. 4x4 posts are normally used to support decks constructed close to ground level. Pier posts should be securely attached to the pier blocks or concrete footing with appropriate connectors.

5. CROSS BRACING: To minimize swaying and lateral movement, cross bracing should be used where pier posts are four feet or higher. 2x4 or 2x6 material is generally used, nailed to the lower portion of one post and the upper portion of an adjacent post. The bracing pattern will vary, depending on the design of the deck and local building code requirements.

D. BEAMS AND JOISTS

1. BEAM CONSTRUCTION: Two types of beam construction can be used. Double beam, with 2-inch thick boards nailed to each side of the pier posts; single beam, with a 4-inch thick board nailed to the top of the pier post.

2. BEAM SIZE AND SPACING: The size and spacing beams should be determined prior to construction of the piers and pier post installation. The distance between beams is determined by joist size and spacing.

3. JOIST SIZE AND SPACING: Joists are used to support the deck flooring. The size of the joists depends on spacing of the support beams. The spacing of Joists is determined by the structural strength of the deck boards. To avoid spring in the deck boards, 2-inch thick redwood should be supported a maximum distance of 30 inches and 1-inch thick boards a maximum distance of every 12 inches. A 2x6 Douglas fir placed on edge will span six feet without spring or deflection.

4. JOIST PLACEMENT: Joists can be placed on top of, or hung between, beams depending on the design of the deck structure, and should he securely attached to the beams with appropriate connectors.

5. JOIST BLOCKING: Deck joists should be supported laterally with blocking at regular intervals. A board nailed between the joists on the top of the beam is one acceptable method of blocking.

E. LEDGER BOARDS

1. A ledger board is used to support the ends of the joists in place of a beam when a deck is attached to a building and the joists run perpendicular to a wall. The ledger board should be set at an elevation low enough below doors so water cannot run into the structure when the deck flooring is in place.

2. Boards 2-inch thick by the width of the beams are usually used for ledgers.

3. Flashing should be installed between the ledger board and the structure and/or a formed piece of flashing placed on top of the ledger board, to provide moisture protection.

4. Ledger boards should be bolted to a joist or beam behind the wall surface at the same elevation as the beams, using 3/8-inch lag bolts every two feet. Bolts should penetrate the support approximately two-thirds its depth.

F. DECK FLOORING

Deck boards should be installed with joints over support beams or joists. Boards should be laid with a maximum 1/8- inch space between adjacent boards. Wet lumber should be spaced closer, or tight, to allow for shrinkage. Boards should be securely nailed with two 6-penny galvanized common nails at each joint or end, and at each supporting member.

G. DECK TRIM

1. A trim board or facia should be installed on the exposed edges of the deck, to conceal beam and joist ends.

2. The position of the trim or facia should be determined by the design and layout of the beams and joists.

3. The trim board can be nailed under the deck boards, allowing for a slight cantilever (one inch) of the deck boards, or can be nailed to the deck boards flush with the finish surface.

4. Blocking should be installed to prevent warping or twisting of the trim boards.

H. TERMITE PROTECTION

Flashing should be installed at all points, including beams, joists, ledger boards, deck boards, handrails or guardrails, and wooden planters attached to a structure.

I. STAIRS AND HANDRAILS

When required, stairs and handrails should be constructed to be compatible with the deck design and constructed in compliance with local building code requirements.
REFER TO WOOD STAIRS FOR SPECIFIC CONSTRUCTION REQUIREMENTS

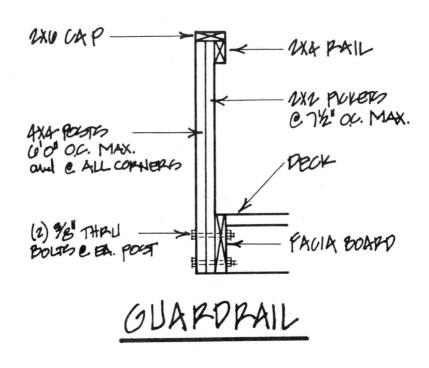

GUARDRAIL

J. GUARDRAILS

1. Depending on the elevation of the deck, guardrails may or may not be required. Section 1711 of the Uniform Building Code requires guardrails be installed on all decks which are more than 30 inches above grade.

2. Guardrails should be 42 inches minimum height for non-residential properties and 36 inches minimum height for residential property. Guardrails should be constructed with intermediate rails or vertical elements spaced so a six-inch sphere cannot pass through the openings.

3. Guardrails should be compatible with the deck design and be constructed in compliance with local building code requirements.

3.06 WOOD GARDEN STAIRS
A. GRADES OF LUMBER

All heart redwood and pressure treated lumber rated for ground contact are the only acceptable lumbers to be used in the construction of wood stairs that are constructed on or near the ground.

B. SUPPORT

Stairs should be supported at the lower end on a concrete slab or curb or, if freestanding, on concrete pier blocks. The upper end of stairs should be attached to another structure or supported on pier blocks. The maximum spacing between supports is six feet.

C. PIER BLOCKS AND POSTS
REFER TO WOOD DECKS FOR SPECIFIC CONSTRUCTION REQUIREMENTS

D. STRINGERS

1. Stringers should be 2x12 lumber and should be securely nailed or bolted to the pier posts.
2. Stairs up to 36 inches in width can be supported with one pair of stringers. Stairs exceeding 36 inches in width require additional stringers, evenly spaced.

E. RISER/TREAD RATIO

1. The height of risers should be not less than four inches nor greater than seven inches, and should not vary more than 3/8 inch in any given run of stairs.
2. The width of treads should be not less than 11 inches and should not vary more than 3/8 inch in any given run of stairs. PRIVATE RESIDENTIAL EXCEPTION allows for eight-inch maximum riser height and nine-inch minimum tread width.
3. For easy ascent, a six-inch riser is recommended.
4. Normal riser/tread ratios can be arrived at by using the following formula: Two times the riser plus tread equals 26 inches, plus or minus.

F. RISER FACE

Open or closed risers may be used in the construction of stairs.

G. TREADS

Tread boards should be all heart redwood, 2-inch thick by desired width, securely fastened to the stringers with galvanized nails.

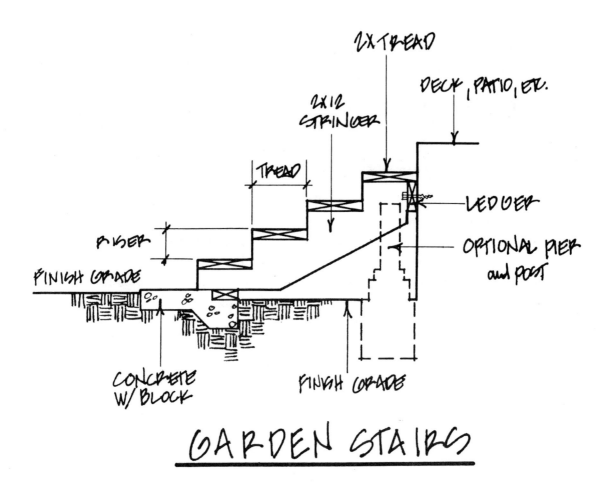

GARDEN STAIRS

H. HANDRAILS

1. On residential property, stairways having four or more risers are required to have a handrail.

2. Handrails should be constructed similar to guardrails with the following exceptions:

   a. Handrails should be not less than 30 inches or more than 34 inches above the nosing of the stair tread.

   b. Handrails should be installed the full length of the stairs and should extend at least six inches beyond the top and bottom risers.

   c. The handgrip portion of the handrail should be 1-1/4 to 2 inches in width, should have a smooth surface, and when mounted on a wall should be a minimum of $1-1^{1}/_{2}$ inches from the wall.

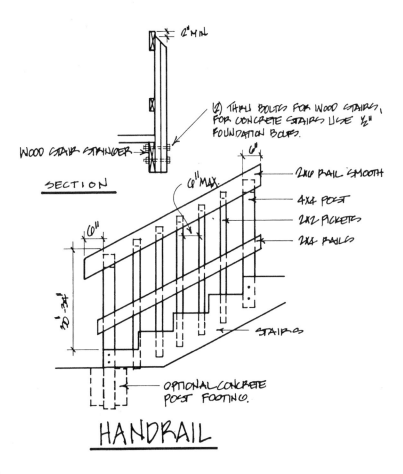

HANDRAIL

3.07 BENCHES

A. GRADES OF LUMBER

1. Posts should be all-heart redwood.

2. Bench seat should be a minimum of construction heart redwood or equivalent grade of lumber.

3. All trim should be the same grade as the bench seat.

B. POST SUPPORTS

Benches can be constructed as part of a wood deck, in a concrete or masonry patio, or free-standing in the landscape. Each application requires different methods of post support.

1. POST SIZING AND SPACING: Posts should be of sufficient size to support the bench, and properly spaced to prevent any sag of the bench seat.

2. WOOD DECK: The bench posts should extend through the deck flooring to the bottom of the deck support structure. The posts should be attached securely to the beams, joists, and blocking as needed.

3. CONCRETE OR MASONRY PATIO: The bench posts should be set in 12-inch diameter by 24-inch deep holes filled with concrete. To avoid the possibility of decay, wood posts can be set on heavy-duty metal post anchors embedded in the concrete pier hole, or galvanized metal pipe or tubing posts can be used.

4. FREE-STANDING: Posts should be set in 12-inch diameter by 36-inch deep concrete filled holes.

47

C. BENCH SEAT SUPPORTS

Two bench seat supports, of sufficient size to support the bench, should be bolted to the posts.

D. BENCH SEAT

1. The bench seat can be prefabricated or built in place.

2. Seat should be constructed of 2-inch thick material of an appropriate grade and surface finish.

E. TRIM

The understructure of the bench should be concealed with appropriate trim or facia, using material to match the bench.

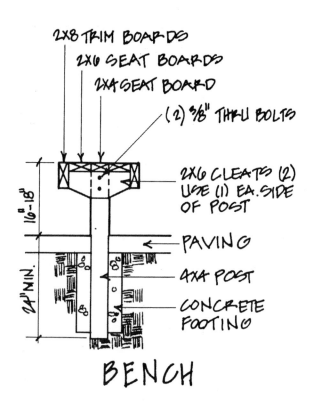

2X8 TRIM BOARDS
2X6 SEAT BOARDS
2X4 SEAT BOARD
(2) 3/8" THRU BOLTS
2X6 CLEATS (2) USE (1) EA. SIDE OF POST
16"-18"
PAVING
4X4 POST
CONCRETE FOOTING
24" MIN.

BENCH

3.08 ARBORS

Free-standing or attached, arbors can provide both decorative and functional elements in the landscape. The design of an arbor and local building code requirements will determine the type and dimensions of lumber used. Since arbors are considered a structure, most building departments require a permit for construction.

A. GRADES OF LUMBER

1. Lumber in contact with the ground should be all heart redwood or pressure treated lumber rated for ground contact.

2. Structural grade redwood, Douglas fir, or other approved species may be used for beams, rafters, and top boards.

3. Lumber may be surfaced, rough, or a combination of both.

B. LAYOUT

Arbors should be carefully laid out to properly locate the support posts.

C. SUPPORT

Free-standing arbors should have shear support in two directions. Attached arbors should be firmly anchored to a ledger board bolted to a stable structure. Ledger boards should be installed in the same manner as deck ledgers.

D. POSTS

1. All posts should be truly vertical and equally spaced.

2. Sizing and spacing of the posts vary, depending on the design, size, and spacing of the beams.

3. Post size should be minimum 4x4 spaced, usually not more than eight feet apart.

4. Depending on the design, arbor posts may be set in concrete or installed on top of a concrete slab or foundation pad with appropriate metal post anchors and adequate shear support (recommended method) or attached to the support structure of a wood deck.

5. Post holes for posts set in the ground should be a minimum of 12 inches in diameter and a minimum of 48 inches deep for an eight-foot high arbor. Concrete should not enclose the bottom of the post.

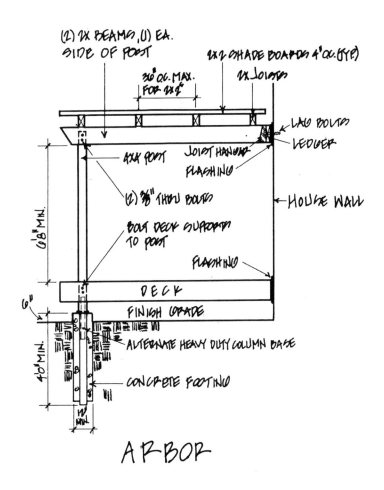

ARBOR

E. BEAMS

The dimensions of arbor beams vary, depending on the design, type of construction, spacing of support posts, and the weight of the lumber to be supported.

1. SINGLE BEAM: A single beam, usually 4x6 to 4x12, set on top of the posts and securely anchored to the posts, using appropriate connectors.

2. DOUBLE BEAM: Two beams, usually 2x6 to 2x12, one attached on each side of the posts and securely bolted together through the posts. Double beams should be blocked at midpoint of each span.

F. RAFTERS

The dimensions of arbor rafters vary, depending on the spacing of the beams and the size of the top boards, if any.

1. Rafters should be spaced four feet on center when using 2x4 lumber on edge and six feet on center when using 2x6 lumber on edge. Rafters may be installed with closer spacing, depending on the design, particularly when top boards are not used.

2. Rafters should be nailed to each beam, and any necessary joining should be made only over a beam.

G. TOP BOARDS

Various depths of shade can be created when top boards are installed on an arbor. 2x2 lumber is commonly used.

1. Spacing of top boards depends on the density of shade desired. Depending on the exposure, a two-inch spacing between boards will provide moderate shade.

2. All top boards should be securely nailed to each rafter.

3.09 WOOD RETAINING WALLS

A. GRADE OF LUMBER

All lumber used to construct retaining walls should be all heart redwood or pressure treated lumber rated for ground contact. Lumber can be surfaced or rough finish.

B. STRUCTURAL DESIGN

1. Dimensions of posts and boards used in the construction of wood retaining walls vary, depending on the soil type and surcharge on the wall.

2. Wood retaining walls exceeding 36 inches in height should be designed by a licensed engineer.

C. POSTS

1. Post holes should be a minimum of 12 inches in diameter and a minimum of 42 inches deep for a 36-inch high wall.

2. Walls up to a height of 36 inches usually require a minimum of 4x4 posts set in concrete, spaced a maximum of four feet on center. Concrete should not encase the post at the bottom of the hole.

D. BOARDS

1. A minimum of 2-inch thick lumber should be used for walls up to 36 inches in height.

2. Boards should be installed on the earth side of the posts and nailed with galvanized nails.

3. If boards are placed on the front side of the posts, each board should be secured to the posts with two galvanized bolts and appropriate washers.

E. CAP

1. Wall caps are usually constructed of the same species of wood as the wall.

2. To avoid cupping of the cap boards, two or three 1/4-inch deep cuts should be made the length of the underside of the cap.

F. DRAINAGE

All walls should be relieved of hydrostatic pressure. This should be accomplished by one of the following methods:

1. Weep holes, a minimum of one inch in diameter, can be drilled at the bottom of wall boards every four feet. One cubic foot of 3/4-inch drain rock should be placed behind each hole.

2. Perforated drain pipe, encased in drain rock and filter fabric, can be placed at the bottom of the backside of the wall.

3. Retaining wall boards can be attached to the posts with ±1/2-inch spacings between the boards and the wall backfilled with drain rock. This can be done in conjunction with the installation of a perforated drainpipe.

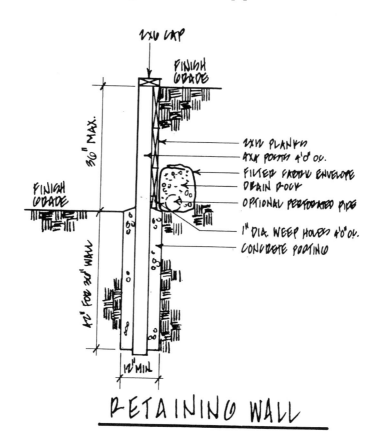

RETAINING WALL

3.10 PLANTER BOXES

A. GRADES OF LUMBER
All lumber should be all heart redwood or pressure treated lumber rated for ground contact.

B. CONSTRUCTION
Planter boxes should be constructed with the same methods used for low retaining walls.

C. DRAINAGE
All planter boxes should be provided with adequate drainage.

3.11 HEADER BOARDS

A. GRADES OF LUMBER
1. HEADERS: Construction heart redwood or pressure treated lumber rated for ground contact, sized as required.

2. STAKES: 1x2 construction heart redwood, 12 to 18 inches long,

B. LAYOUT
All headers should be laid true to line and grade.

C. STRAIGHT HEADERS
1. Headers should be 2x4 lumber laid on edge. Material can be surfaced or rough finish.

2. Stakes should be spaced four feet on center maximum, with two at each joint, and securely nailed to the header with galvanized nails.

D. HEADERS WITH A SLIGHT CURVE
1. Two 1x4 boards should be tightly laminated, with joints staggered a minimum of 48 inches apart.

2. Stakes should be spaced three feet on center maximum and at each joint, and securely nailed to the header with galvanized nails.

E. HEADERS WITH A STRONG CURVE
1. Four or more 3/8x4 inch boards should be tightly laminated, with joints staggered a minimum of 48 inches apart

2. Laminations should be nailed a minimum of 12 inches on center.

3. Stakes should be spaced a minimum of three feet on center and at each joint, and securely nailed to the header with galvanized nails.

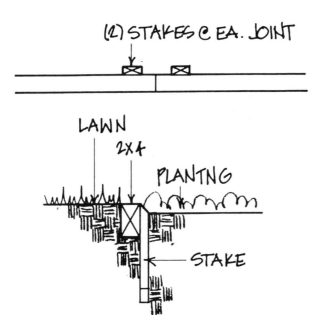

(2) STAKES @ EA. JOINT

LAWN

2X4

PLANTNG

STAKE

HEADER BOARD / STRAIGHT LINE

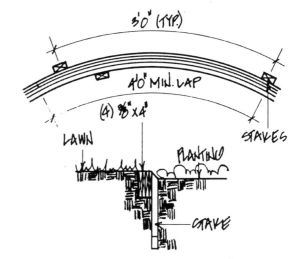

3'0" (TYP.)

4'0" MIN. LAP

(4) ⅜"X4"

LAWN

PLANTNG

STAKES

STAKE

HEADER BOARD / STRONG CURVE

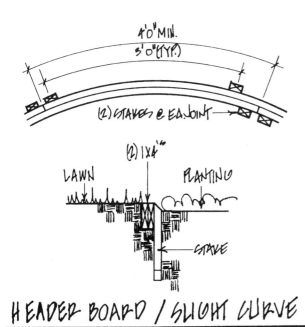

4'0" MIN.

3'0"(TYP.)

(2) STAKES @ EA. JOINT

(2) 1X4"

LAWN

PLANTING

STAKE

HEADER BOARD / SLIGHT CURVE

PART I – GENERAL

1.01	DESCRIPTION
1.02	WORK INCLUDED
1.03	QUALITY ASSURANCE
1.04	REFERENCES
1.05	SUBMITTALS
1.06	EXISTING CONDITIONS
1.07	SCHEDULING
1.08	CONTRACTOR RESPONSIBILITY

PART 2 – PRODUCTS

2.01	BASE MATERIALS
2.02	REINFORCEMENT
2.03	CONCRETE MIX
2.04	EXPANSION JOINTS
2.05	AGGREGATES FOR SEEDED EXPOSED CONCRETE
2.06	WATERPROOFING PRODUCTS

PART 3 – EXECUTION

3.01	GENERAL REQUIREMENTS
3.02	CONCRETE FOOTINGS
3.03	CONCRETE WALLS
3.04	DRIVEWAYS
3.05	PATIOS
3.06	WALKWAYS
3.07	CONCRETE GARDEN STAIRS
3.08	CONCRETE MOW STRIPS

1.01 DESCRIPTION

Concrete construction provides both functional and esthetic elements in the landscape.

1.02 WORK INCLUDED

This section includes the construction of concrete footings, walls, driveways, patios, walkways, garden stairs, and mow strips.

The provisions of SECTION I- GENERAL REQUIREMENTS apply to the work in this section as though written herein in full.

1.03 QUALITY ASSURANCE

Permits may be required for concrete construction, depending on local building code requirements.

1.04 REFERENCES

CALTRANS STANDARD SPECIFICATIONS, Current Edition

PORTLAND CEMENT ASSOCIATION publications

UNIFORM BUILDING CODE, Current Edition

1.05 SUBMITTALS

Samples of concrete finish, color, or gravel for seeded exposed concrete may be required.

1.06 EXISTING CONDITIONS

Methods of construction and structural details vary, depending on soil type and whether the site is cut or fill.

1.07 SCHEDULING

A. All related grading should be completed, all underground piping installed, and necessary sleeving placed prior to commencement of concrete construction.

B. All concrete construction should be completed prior to the installation of irrigation and planting.

1.08 CONTRACTOR RESPONSIBILITY

Contractor should provide proper drainage on and off all flat concrete surfaces.

2.01 BASE MATERIALS
A. SAND
Clean, washed sand, uniform in size and texture, and free of clay lumps or large stones.

B. GRAVEL
3/8 inch pea gravel.

C. AGGREGATE SUB-BASE
Should conform to the grading and quality requirements set forth in CalTrans Standard Specifications.

2.02 REINFORCEMENT
A. STEEL REBAR
Deformed, new billet steel bars. Size of rebar will depend on the spacing of reinforcement, the depth of concrete, and structural requirements.

B. TIE WIRE
Standard AWG #14 gauge wire.

C. WELDED WIRE MESH
AWG #10 gauge wire welded together to form a 6x6 inch mesh.

2.03 CONCRETE MIX
A. CEMENT
Standard portland cement, domestic grey, Type 11.

B. AGGREGATES
1. All aggregates should be free of all animal or vegetable matter.

2. FINE: Clean, washed river sand or aggregates manufactured from crushed rock, with sharp particles graded from #100 sieve to 1/4 inch.

3. COARSE: Gravel graded from 1/4 to 3/4 inch.

C. ADMIXTURES
If used, admixtures should be the proper type for the use intended (hardening, color, etc.), and used only per the manufacturer's specifications.

2.04 EXPANSION JOINTS
Wood, metal, or composition strips, minimum 1/4-inch wide by the depth of the concrete.

2.05 AGGREGATES FOR SEEDED EXPOSED CONCRETE
Smooth, attractive gravel quarried from ocean beaches or riverbeds. Aggregates sized from 1/4 to 1-1/2 inch are generally used for seeded exposed concrete. Many colors are available.

2.06 WATERPROOFING PRODUCTS

Many types of waterproofing products are available, including liquids or pastes, which can be painted on the surface of a wall, and membranes, which can be attached to the surface of a wall. Such products should be used per the manufacturer's recommendations.

3.01 GENERAL REQUIREMENTS

A. FORMING

Wood or metal forms should be used for all concrete installations, with the exception of concrete footings poured in firm, unyielding earth. Forms should be placed with a smooth side toward the concrete, and adequately staked and braced for maximum load, to retain their shape and position during the placement of the concrete. All forming material should be easily strippable once the concrete is sufficiently cured.

B. BURIED INSERTS

All reinforcement, knock-outs, conduits, pipes, or other inserts that are to remain buried in finished concrete should be accurately placed and securely fastened in place. The requirements for such inserts and their proper location in any forms should be confirmed prior to concrete placement.

C. REINFORCEMENT

All laps of steel rebar should be 30 diameters of the rod and should be tied at intersections not farther apart than 24 inches. Steel rebar should be a minimum of two inches from the finish edge of all concrete. Reinforcement should not continue through expansion joint or control joint. If a tie is required, use dowels or keyed joint.

D. EXPANSION JOINTS AND CONTROL JOINTS

Used to minimize or control cracking of the concrete, expansion joints or control joints should be spaced a maximum of 10 feet in both directions and at all corners. Expansion joints should he installed in all locations where concrete abuts a structure or concrete slab. Control joints should be made with a power saw or scoring tool and form a weakened plane one-fifth the thickness of the concrete slab.

E. MOISTURE LEVEL OF SUB-BASE AND BASE

When the sub-base is an expansive type soil, NEVER pour concrete until the soil has been completely moistened and has expanded. Prior to pouring concrete, the base material should be moistened so it will not wick moisture out of the concrete and interfere with proper curing.

F. CONCRETE PLACEMENT

All concrete should be placed in a continuous manner between stopping points and compacted to obtain a reasonably smooth surface. Flat surfaces should be leveled with a "bull float" or similar equipment, and all exposed edges finished with a slight round or bull nose. Finish troweling should be done when the surface has lost its water sheen, but before hardening.

G. WALL FINISHES

Many finishes can be used, ranging from smooth finish to a seeded exposed sandblast finish, plus the numerous textures that are available by using preformed form liners. Concrete walls can also be finished with stucco to match a building exterior finish.

H. FLAT FINISHES

The plasticity of wet concrete allows a wide range of finishes on concrete flatwork.

1. TROWELED: The surface of the concrete is smoothed with a finishing trowel to a polished finish.

2. BROOM FINISH: A fine broom is drawn over the surface when the concrete is almost hardened to leave a slight texture.

3. SAND FINISH: The concrete is lightly washed to remove the glaze left by the trowel.

4. WASHED FINISH: The concrete surface is more heavily washed to expose some of the aggregate in the concrete.

5. ROCK SALT FINISH: Rock salt is lightly and evenly seeded over the wet concrete and lightly troweled into the surface. After the concrete has hardened, the rock salt is swept and/or washed out of the concrete to leave a pattern of small pits.

6. SEEDED EXPOSED FINISH: Decorative aggregate is evenly seeded on the surface of the wet concrete and troweled into the surface. When the concrete is almost hardened, the surface is lightly washed and broomed to expose the decorative aggregate. Care must be taken not to overexpose the aggregate.

7. STAMPED FINISH: Various patterns and textures can be stamped into the surface of the concrete. This process requires the use of special stamping molds. The surface of the concrete is often color-coated prior to stamping.

I. CURING

Concrete should be kept damp at least 72 hours before forms are removed. Moisture in the concrete may be retained by using sprinklers, waterproof paper without asphalt or other coatings, straw, sand, or other approved material.

J. FORM REMOVAL

Extreme care should be exercised when removing forms to prevent damage to the concrete, especially at corners and openings. Wood forms which may have expanded during the curing period require additional care during removal.

3.02 CONCRETE FOOTINGS

A. DIMENSIONS

The depth and width of concrete footings will vary, depending on the soil type, construction methods, and height of the wall.

B. SUB-GRADE

The sub-grade for footings should be free of organic matter, large clay lumps, or stones larger than one inch and compacted to 95% relative density.

C. FORMS

Forming for footings should be true to line and grade, well staked, and braced. Forms may not be required, on one or both sides, if the footing is excavated in firm, unyielding earth.

D. REINFORCEMENT

1. Horizontal reinforcement should be two #4 (1/2-inch) steel rebar, eight inches on center, for each 12-inch width of footing.

2. When required for wall construction, vertical reinforcement should be installed in the footings as required for the wall reinforcement.

E. CONCRETE

The concrete should be a minimum of 5-sack mix with 3/4-inch aggregate or 6-sack mix with 3/8-inch aggregate.

3.03 CONCRETE WALLS
A. FORMING

Forms should be 2-inch surfaced Douglas fir and/or 3/4-inch plywood. Adequate wall ties and spacers should be used to hold the forms in place, and the forms should be staked and braced firmly to resist movement.

B. REINFORCEMENT

1. Reinforcement of free-standing or retaining walls should meet all local building code requirements.

2. Minimum vertical reinforcement for a three-foot high free-standing wall is one #4 (1/2-inch) rebar, 24 inches on center; minimum horizontal reinforcement is one #4 rebar, 12 inches on center. Lap all joints 30 diameters and tie vertical and horizontal rebar at all crossovers.

C. CONCRETE PLACEMENT

1. Concrete should be minimum 5-sack mix with 3/4-inch gravel or 6-sack mix with 3/8-inch gravel.

2. The concrete should be placed evenly along the length of the wall and tamped or vibrated to remove any and all voids.

3. Finished surfaces should be free of rock pockets, form tie-holes, or other defects. Any such defects should be immediately repaired with a concrete slurry of the same mix and color as the original concrete. Defects larger than six inches in any direction should be chipped out and repaired or the entire concrete section removed and replaced.

D. DRAINAGE

All walls that retain soil are subject to hydrostatic pressure when the soil becomes saturated. It is essential to provide adequate drainage to prevent failure of the wall.

1. The preferred method, to provide proper drainage, is the placement of rigid PVC perforated drainpipe, drain rock, and filter fabric behind the wall. The drainpipe should be placed at the back of the wall footing or on top of the footing at an

elevation which will ensure adequate slope so water will drain to the point of discharge.

2. An alternate method to provide drainage is the installation of one-inch weep holes every four feet near the base of the wall. Drain rock should be placed the full length of the wall, covering all weep holes.

3. All drain rock should be surrounded with filter fabric to prevent the rock from becoming clogged with silt washing out of the surrounding soil.

E. WALL SEALING

All walls should be sealed or waterproofed on the soil side, to prevent moisture from coming through the wall and the resulting efflorescence on the face of the wall. The selected wall sealer should be applied per the manufacturer's recommendations.

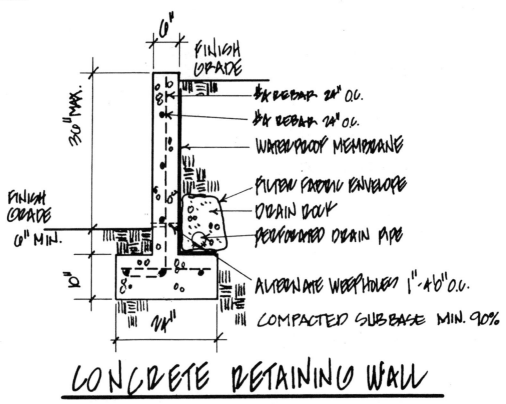

3.04 DRIVEWAYS

A. SUB-GRADE

Driveways should be sub-graded to proper depth; the sub-grade free of organic matter, large clay lumps, or stones larger than one inch in diameter; and compacted to 95% relative density.

B. BASE

Two inches of sand or pea gravel or four inches of aggregate base compacted to 90% compaction.

C. FORMING

Forms should be set true to line and grade, and to allow for proper drainage, minimum 1% for smooth finish surface and minimum 2% for seeded exposed surfaces.

D. REINFORCEMENT

Driveways should be reinforced with a minimum of #4 steel rebar 12 to 18 inches on center in both directions, tied at each crossover, or with 6x6x#10 welded wire mesh.

E. EXPANSION JOINTS

Appropriate expansion joints or control joints should be installed at intervals of 10 feet maximum and at any junction of other concrete slabs, walls, or structures.

F. CONCRETE

Concrete should be minimum 5-sack mix with 3/4-inch aggregate or 6-sack mix with 3/8-inch aggregate, a minimum of 4 inches thick, and finished as desired.

3.05 PATIOS

A. SUB-GRADE

The sub-grade should be free of organic matter, large clay lumps, and stone larger than one inch, and should be compacted to 90% relative density.

B. BASE

Concrete base should be a minimum of two inches of sand or pea gravel.

C. FORMING

The forms should be set true to line and grade, and adequately staked and braced for maximum load. Forms should be set to provide a minimum 1% slope for broom finish concrete and 2% slope for exposed aggregate concrete.

D. REINFORCEMENT

Patios and swimming pool decks should be reinforced with 6x6x#10 welded wire mesh or #3 (3/8-inch) steel rebar, tied 24 inches on center in both directions.

E. EXPANSION JOINTS

Appropriate expansion joints or control joints should be installed at intervals of 10 feet maximum in both directions, at all corners, and at any junction of other concrete slabs or permanent structures.

F. CONCRETE

Concrete should be minimum 5-sack mix with 3/4-inch aggregate or 6-sack mix with 3/8-inch aggregate, a minimum of 3-1/2 inches thick and finished as desired.

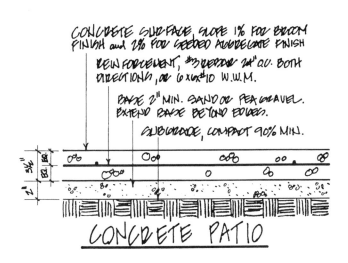

3.06 WALKWAYS

A. SUB-GRADE

Sub-grade should be free of organic matter, large clay lumps, or stones larger than one inch, and should be compacted to 90% relative density.

B. BASE

Concrete base should be a minimum of two inches of sand or pea gravel.

C. FORMING

Walkways should be formed with appropriate form material installed true to line and grade and set for proper drainage, with a minimum 1% cross slope, adequately staked, and braced for maximum load.

D. REINFORCEMENT

Walkways should be reinforced with 6x6x#10 welded wire mesh or #3 (3/8-inch) steel rebar, tied 24 inches on center in both directions.

E. EXPANSION JOINTS

Appropriate expansion joints or control joints should be placed at maximum intervals of two times the width of the walk.

F. CONCRETE

Concrete should be minimum 5-sack mix with 3/4-inch aggregate or 6-sack mix with 3/8-inch aggregate, finished as desired.

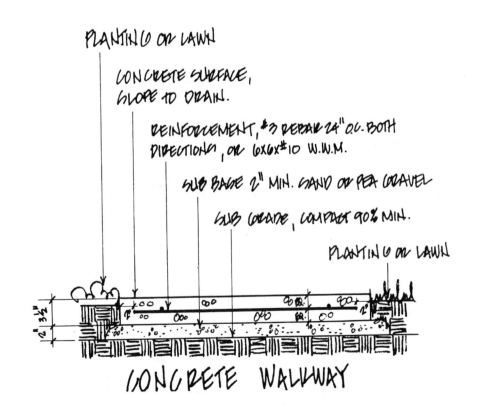

CONCRETE WALKWAY

3.07 CONCRETE GARDEN STAIRS

A. RISER/TREAD RATIO

REFER TO WOOD CONSTRUCTION - GARDEN STAIRS FOR SPECIFIC CON-STRUCTION REQUIREMENTS

B. SUB-GRADE

The sub-grade should be excavated to undisturbed soil, should be free of organic matter, large clay lumps, or stones larger than one inch, and should be compacted to 90% relative density.

C. BASE

A minimum of two inches of sand or pea gravel should be used as a base for the concrete.

D. FORMING

Stairs should be formed with 2-inch thick Douglas fir. Forms should be set level and true to line and grade, and adequately staked and braced for maximum load. Riser forms should be reinforced with strongbacks, installed a minimum of four feet on center. Each thread should be formed to allow for proper drainage.

E. REINFORCEMENT

Stairs should be reinforced with #3 (3/8-inch) steel rebar 12 inches on center in both directions. Steel rebar should be a minimum of two inches from the edge of the concrete.

F. EXPANSION JOINTS

Expansion joints should be installed in stairs exceeding 10 feet in width, and at the top and/or bottom of stairs connected to concrete patios, walkways, or structures.

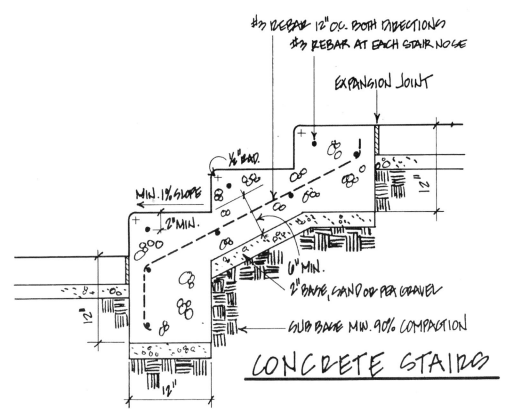

#3 REBAR 12" O.C. BOTH DIRECTIONS
#3 REBAR AT EACH STAIR NOSE
EXPANSION JOINT
1/4" RAD.
MIN. 1% SLOPE
2" MIN.
12"
6" MIN.
2" BASE, SAND OR PEA GRAVEL
SUB BASE MIN. 90% COMPACTION
12"
12"

CONCRETE STAIRS

G. CONCRETE

Concrete should be minimum 5-sack mix with 3/4-inch aggregate or 6-sack mix with 3/8-inch aggregate, finished as desired.

H. HANDRAILS

REFER TO WOOD CONSTRUCTION- GARDEN STAIRS FOR SPECIFIC CONSTRUCTION REQUIREMENTS

3.08 CONCRETE MOW STRIPS

A. SUB-GRADE

The sub-grade should be free of organic matter, large clay lumps, or stones larger than one inch, and compacted to 90% relative density.

B. BASE

The base should be a minimum of two inches of sand or pea gravel.

C. FORMING

1. Concrete mow strips should be a minimum of seven inches wide by four inches deep.

2. Forms should be true to line and grade, and adequately staked and braced to maintain a uniform line, with the top of the finished mow strip formed to be at the same level as the adjacent turf.

D. REINFORCEMENT

Concrete mow strips should be reinforced with one #3 rebar centered in the concrete.

E. EXPANSION JOINTS

Appropriate expansion joints or control joints should be placed at a maximum of 10-foot intervals.

F. CONCRETE

Concrete should be minimum 5-sack mix with 3/4-inch aggregate or 6-sack mix with 3/8-inch aggregate, finished as desired.

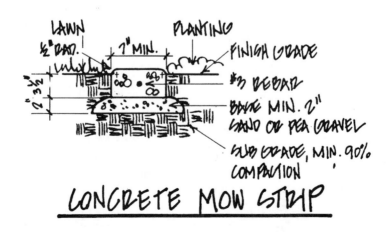

CONCRETE MOW STRIP

PART 1 – GENERAL

PART 2 – PRODUCTS

PART 3 – EXECUTION

1.01 DESCRIPTION

The construction of functional and esthetic landscape elements, using brick, concrete building units and pavers, natural stone, and tile.

1.02 WORK INCLUDED

This section includes the construction of masonry and stone walls, and the installation of masonry, stone, and tile paving.

The provisions of SECTION 1- GENERAL REQUIREMENTS apply to the work in this section as though written herein in full.

1.03 QUALITY ASSURANCE

Permits may be required for the construction of masonry structures and for masonry retaining walls, depending on the height of the wall and local building code requirements.

1.04 REFERENCES

PORTLAND CEMENT ASSOCIATION publications
UNIFORM BUILDING CODE, Current Edition

1.05 SCHEDULING

All masonry construction should be completed prior to the installation of irrigation and planting.

PART 2 — PRODUCTS

2.01 BASE MATERIALS

2.02 REINFORCEMENT   *REFER TO CONCRETE CONSTRUCTION- PART 2*

2.03 CONCRETE MIX

2.04 MORTAR

Mortar should be a uniform mixture of one part cement and three parts clean, sharp, well-graded sand, with one-quarter-part lime added.

2.05 GROUT

Grout used for reinforced walls should be a uniform mixture of one part portland cement, three parts sand, and two parts 3/8-inch gravel.

2.06 MASONRY UNITS

A. BRICK

Building and paving brick are manufactured in many sizes and colors.

1. The size of common brick is approximately 2-5/8 by 3-5/8 by 7-5/8 inches.

2. Terra cotta or "red" color is typical.

3. Grades and sizes are listed in ASTM C62.

B. CONCRETE BUILDING BLOCK

Concrete building blocks are manufactured in a variety of sizes and shapes from cement, sand, and lightweight aggregate, and are generally grey in color.

1. Common sizes are 4, 6, and 8 inches wide by 4 or 8 inches high and 16 inches long. 8x8x16 inches is standard. All dimensions are nominal, allowing for a 3/8-inch mortar joint.

2. Grades and sizes are listed in ASTM C90 and/or C1 39.

C. SLUMPSTONE BLOCK

Resembling adobe block, sandstone-colored slumpstone blocks are manufactured from cement, sand, and lightweight aggregate. Dimensions of slumpstone block are the same as those for concrete building block.

D. CONCRETE PAVERS

Manufactured in many shapes, sizes, and colors, concrete unit pavers are designed to interlock. They are available in different thickness for vehicular and pedestrian traffic applications.

2.07 STONE

A. QUARRIED STONE

1. GRANITE: A hard, dense stone used for paving, curbing, building veneer, and for rip-rap. Granite comes in many colors. It is available rough or cut (such as San Francisco cobble) and as a cut-stone paving unit in various sizes that can be polished if desired.

2. LIMESTONE: Softer than granite, limestone is easy to work with and can be used for coping, paving, veneer, and dry stone walls. Limestone ranges in color from eggshell white to light grey.

3. SANDSTONE: More durable than limestone, sandstone is used for the same purposes as limestone. The most common sandstones are earthen in color, ranging from deep ochre to sienna or umber.

4. ARIZONA FLAGSTONE: A soft to medium hard stone typically used in flat installations. Arizona flagstone is tan to red in color and usually available in large, irregular pieces, 3/4 to 2 inches thick.

B. FIELDSTONE

Found naturally in fields or along streams and rivers, fieldstone is used for paving, curbing, and dry or mortared stone walls.

2.08 TILE PAVERS

Many types of tile paving units are used in landscape construction, including glazed or unglazed clay and ceramic tiles. Tile pavers are available in a wide variety of dimensions and colors. All tile used for landscape applications should be specified for outdoor use by the manufacturer.

PART 3 — EXECUTION

3.01 GENERAL CONSTRUCTION REQUIREMENTS

A. FOOTINGS

All concrete footings should be sized and reinforced as required to properly support the wall, and installed in soil trenches, with the bottom of the trench compacted to 95%. Reinforcing steel, where required, should project at least 30 diameters of the rod dimension above the footing. Footings should have a clean, level surface prior to constructing walls.

B. CONCRETE SUB-BASE

Reinforced concrete sub-base slabs should be installed on a soil base compacted to 95% relative density.
REFER TO CONCRETE CONSTRUCTION - PART 3

C. REINFORCEMENT

Vertical and horizontal rods should be tied at a minimum of 18 inches in each direction with annealed iron wire. Horizontal reinforcement in low brick walls may be welded wire mesh embedded in the mortar joint. Any laps of reinforcement rods should be a minimum of 30 diameters of the rod.

D. BRICK CONSTRUCTION

All brick should be clean and free of dirt and thoroughly wetted, but not soaked, so the water in the mortar is sufficient to allow proper placement. Bed and end joints should be full and exposed. joints on brick faces should be struck flush, unless a tooled joint is required.

E. MORTAR

Mortar should be well mixed to a uniform consistency and not used if standing more than two hours. Re-tempering of mortar should not be allowed, except that mortar or "boards" may be re-wet by adding a small amount of water, which can be mixed into the entire batch.

F. MORTAR JOINTS

1. Flush joints should be made by cutting off the mortar flush with the face of the masonry unit.

2. Tooled joints should be made with a metal jointing tool.

3. Raked joints should be recessed approximately 3/8 inch with a jointing tool.

G. GROUT

Grout should be placed in all voids of reinforced brick or concrete masonry unit walls and should be compacted using a blunt-end rod or vibrating tool.

H. CLEANUP

Mortar and/or grout that is spilled on exposed surfaces of masonry should be removed with clean water before stain has been allowed to set. Excessively stained masonry may be cleaned with a diluted solution of muratic acid or masonry cleaner, and should be thoroughly rinsed with clean water.

3.02 BRICK WALLS

A. TYPES OF CONSTRUCTION

1. Brick walls of 12 inches or less may be single-wall construction.

2. Brick walls more than 12 inches in height should be double-wall construction.

B. FOOTINGS

REFER TO CONCRETE CONSTRUCTION - PART 3

C. REINFORCEMENT

Brick walls should be properly reinforced as required by local building code requirements.

D. BRICK INSTALLATION

All brick should be laid plumb, level, and true to line in the desired pattern.

E. GROUTING

The cavity space between double-wall constructed brick walls should be filled with mortar or grout.

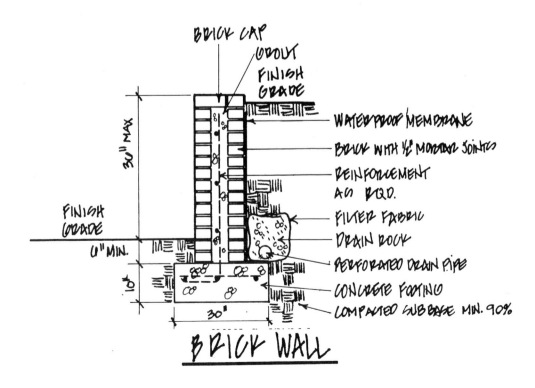

BRICK WALL

F. WALL CAP

Brick walls should be capped with the same brick used in the wall construction, unless otherwise designed. The cap brick is usually laid perpendicular to the wall.

G. DRAINAGE

REFER TO CONCRETE CONSTRUCTION - PART 3 CONCRETE WALLS

H. WALL SEALING

REFER TO CONCRETE CONSTRUCTION - PART 3 CONCRETE WALLS

3.03 CONCRETE BUILDING BLOCK AND SLUMPSTONE WALLS

A. WALL CONSTRUCTION

Concrete building block walls are generally eight inches wide and constructed using standard 8x8x16 block.

B. FOOTINGS

REFER TO CONCRETE CONSTRUCTION- PART 3

C. REINFORCEMENT

Walls 24 to 36 inches high should have #4 reinforcing bars installed 24 inches on center vertically and on 16-inch centers horizontally in the mortar joints. Walls less than 24 inches in height do not require reinforcement except for the top course, unless such walls are surcharged by an earth bank behind them, in which case they should be reinforced as though 48 inches in height.

D. BLOCK INSTALLATION

All block units should be laid in a running bond pattern with a 3/8-inch mortar joint, tooled as desired.

E. GROUTING

All cells should be filled solid with grout mix.

F. WALL CAP

Concrete block walls should be capped with a minimum two-inch cap, unless otherwise designed. Slumpstone walls should be capped with a slumpstone cap.

G. DRAINAGE

REFER TO CONCRETE CONSTRUCTION - PART 3 CONCRETE WALLS

H. SEALING

REFER TO CONCRETE CONSTRUCTION - PART 3 CONCRETE WALLS

I. WALL FINISH

Concrete block walls can be left plain, finished with plaster or stucco, or painted, depending on the desired finish appearance.

3.04 STONE WALLS

A. TYPES OF CONSTRUCTION

Stone walls can be constructed from almost any type of stone, with little or no cutting and trimming, and may be either mortared or dry-stacked construction. Free-standing walls should be double-wall construction with small stone rubble between the wythes. Retaining walls may be single- or double-wall construction, depending on site requirements.

B. FOOTINGS

Mortared stone walls should be constructed on a concrete footing. Dry-stacked walls may be constructed on a concrete footing or set in excavated, compacted soil.

REFER TO CONCRETE CONSTRUCTION - PART 3 CONCRETE FOOTINGS

C. REINFORCEMENT

Due to the generally irregular size and/or shape of stone, reinforcement is usually not possible in stone walls. To achieve structural strength, the bottom of stone walls should be constructed wider at the bottom than at the top. The largest stones should be used for the first course. Bond stones should be laid across the wall to connect the wythes in double walls.

D. MORTARED STONE INSTALLATION

1. Stones should be clean and carefully fitted before mortaring to provide even, overlapping joints, with end joints staggered.

2. The mortar should be slightly stiffer than that used for brick construction, to support the heavier weight of the stones.

3. Mortar joints may be struck flush or tooled. Tooled joints are generally considered most attractive. The mortar can be recessed as much as 1 to 1-1½ inches, depending on the desired finish appearance.

4. Upon completion of installation and proper curing period for the mortar, stone surfaces should be cleaned with a stiff bristle brush. Do not use an acid solution on stone.

E. DRY-STACKED STONE RETAINING WALLS

This type of wall is usually used to retain an existing bank of soil not exceeding three feet in height, and must be constructed with a batter for stability.

1. The bank of soil should be battered one to two inches per foot of wall height.

2. The bottom of the wall should be four to six inches below the finish grade, or below the frost line in cold areas.

3. The first row of stones should be large and heavy enough to anchor the wall to the soil. In all rows including the first, each stone should be placed so it is locked or hooked to the adjacent stones, in all layers including the first.

4. Loose, moist soil should be tamped into all voids between the soil bank and the stones, keying the back side of the stones into the soil bank.

F. DRAINAGE

REFER TO CONCRETE CONSTRUCTION - PART 3 CONCRETE WALLS

3.05 BRICK PAVING

A. TYPES OF CONSTRUCTION

Brick paving may be laid with either dry or wet mortar, or with sand joints in a variety of patterns. All brick paving should be enclosed with a mortared course of brick, a concrete edging strip, or adequately staked header boards.

B. SUB-GRADE

Area should be laid out true to line and grade, excavated to the proper depth with all organic matter, large rocks and clay lumps removed, and compacted to 90% relative density in areas of foot traffic and to 95% relative density in areas of vehicular traffic.

C. BASE

1. Concrete base for areas of vehicular traffic should be a minimum of four inches of concrete laid over a two-inch sub-base of compacted sand or pea gravel.

2. Concrete base for areas of foot and light traffic should be a minimum of two inches of concrete laid over a two-inch sub-base of compacted sand or pea gravel.

3. Sand base for brick-on-sand should be a minimum of ± 1-inch thick, leveled and compacted to 90% relative density.

4. Base should be constructed with a 2% slope.

D. REINFORCEMENT

REFER TO CONCRETE CONSTRUCTION - PART 3 DRIVEWAYS AND PATIOS AND WALKWAYS

E. DRY MORTAR BRICK INSTALLATION

Brick paving installed with dry mortar joints is generally set on a concrete base with a mortared edging course or on a sand base enclosed with adequately staked header boards. To reduce the chance of joint cracking, the sand base should be compacted to 95% relative density.

1. Bricks should be placed with appropriately spaced joints and the joints carefully filled with dry mortar mix. All excess mortar should be brushed off the surface of the brick.

2. The surface should be moistened with a fine spray of water until all mortar mix is well moistened, but not wet.

3. Additional mortar mix should be placed in any joints which settle, and the joints tooled to compress the mortar and form uniform joints.

F. WET MORTAR BRICK INSTALLATION

Brick paving installed with wet mortar joints is generally set on a concrete base.

1. Brick should be placed on a thin, 1/2-inch, mortar bed in the desired pattern with the joints left open.

2. Joints should be filled with wet mortar, using a trowel or mortar bag, after the mortar bed has set up firmly. Care should be taken to avoid excess mortar on the surface.

3. Joints may be finished flush, tooled, or raked.

G. SAND JOINT BRICK INSTALLATION

Brick paving installed with sand joints is generally set on a one- to two-inch compacted sand base.

1. Since some paving patterns require the brick to be twice as long as wide, the choice of brick for this application should be made carefully.

2. Bricks should be laid level with tight joints. Dry, fine sand should be spread over the brick surface and swept into the joints between the bricks.

H. CLEANING

Brick paving installed with dry or wet mortar mix requires some cleaning after installation. The surface should be brushed free of loose mortar. A sponge and water, if used before stains have been allowed to set, will remove most, if not all, mortar stains. A diluted solution of muratic acid or masonry cleaner may be used to remove persistent stains. The brick should be thoroughly rinsed with clear water after using any cleaning solutions.

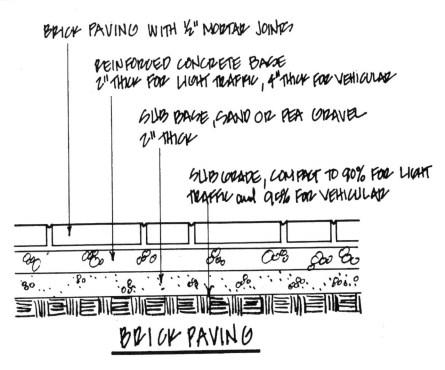

BRICK PAVING WITH ½" MORTAR JOINTS

REINFORCED CONCRETE BASE
2" THICK FOR LIGHT TRAFFIC, 4" THICK FOR VEHICULAR

SUB BASE, SAND OR PEA GRAVEL
2" THICK

SUB GRADE, COMPACT TO 90% FOR LIGHT
TRAFFIC and 95% FOR VEHICULAR

BRICK PAVING

3.06 CONCRETE UNIT PAVERS

A. TYPES OF CONSTRUCTION

Concrete unit pavers are generally installed on a compacted sand base in a variety of patterns. All concrete unit pavers should be enclosed with adequately staked header boards.

B. SUB-GRADE

The area should be laid out true to line and grade. The sub-grade should be undisturbed soil excavated to the proper depth and free of all organic matter, large rocks, and clay lumps, and compacted to 90% relative density.

C. BASE

1. The base should be a minimum of four inches of compacted aggregate base topped with two inches of compacted sand. The sand should be moistened and tamped to form a smooth, level surface. All compaction should be to 90% relative density.

2. The base should be constructed with a 2% slope.

D. INSTALLATION

1. Pavers should be laid true to line and grade in the desired pattern, following the manufacturer's recommendations.

2. Dry, fine sand should be dusted over the concrete paver surface and swept to fill all cracks between the pavers.

3.07 NATURAL STONE PAVING

A. TYPES OF CONSTRUCTION

Natural stone paving may be laid in a variety of patterns, using dry or wet mortar, sand, or soil joints.

B. SUB-GRADE

C. BASE
REFER TO BRICK PAVING

D. REINFORCEMENT

E. INSTALLATION

1. All stone should be laid true to line and grade in the desired pattern.

2. DRY MORTAR: See Brick Paving.

3. WET MORTAR: Stone should be set on a mortar bed and mortar used to connect the stone pieces and fill the joints. Mortar joints should be a maximum of two inches wide and finished as desired. The finished surface should be thoroughly cleaned after mortaring. Acid should not be used to clean the surface of natural stone.

4. SAND JOINTS: Unless the sides of the stone are cut straight and square, sand joints are not recommended.

5. SOIL JOINTS: Natural stone is often set on a compacted soil base, with soil placed between the stones for planting. The width of the joints must be sufficient to allow for root development of the plant material and should be not less than two inches.

3.08 TILE PAVING

A. BASE

The base for tile paving should be the same as used for brick paving, with one exception. If a sand base is used, the base should be a minimum of four inches thick.

B. REINFORCEMENT
REFER TO BRICK PAVING

C. INSTALLATION

1. All tile should be installed per manufacturer's recommendations.

2. Tile should be laid true to line and grade in the desired pattern.

3. MORTAR: Tile paving should be installed with wet mortar, applied with a trowel or mortar bag.

4. JOINTS: Joints between tile pavers should be 1/2-inch tooled joints, unless otherwise specified.

3.09 BRICK MOW STRIPS

A. TYPE OF CONSTRUCTION

Brick mortared on top of a concrete mow strip. Brick mow strips are generally used as a divider between lawn and planting areas.

B. BASE

Brick mow strips should be installed on a concrete sub-base.

REFER TO CONCRETE CONSTRUCTION - PART 3 MOW STRIPS

C. REINFORCEMENT

REFER TO CONCRETE CONSTRUCTION - PART 3 MOW STRIPS

D INSTALLATION

1. Brick should be laid true to line and grade in the desired pattern.

2. Brick should be thoroughly clean and wet and set on a mortar bed, with the joints finished as desired.

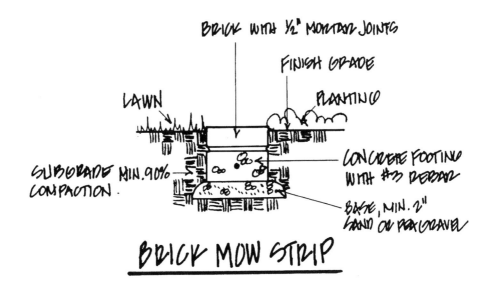

BRICK MOW STRIP

PART 1 – GENERAL

PART 2 – PRODUCTS

PART 3 – EXECUTION

1.01 DESCRIPTION

A landscape irrigation system is any assemblage of special equipment and materials that are designed, manufactured, and installed for controlled dispersion of water from any safe and suitable source, including properly treated wastewater, for the express purpose of irrigation of any and all types of landscape vegetation or the control of dust and/or erosion or other environmental control of any and all landscaped areas.

1.02 WORK INCLUDED

This section includes the supply and installation of pipe and fittings, backflow prevention devices, valves and valve boxes, controllers and control circuits, sprinkler heads and risers, anti-drain valves, booster pumps, moisture sensors, drip irrigation, methods for winterization, and preparation of as-built drawings.

The provisions of SECTION 1– GENERAL REQUIREMENTS apply to the work under this section as though written herein in full.

1.03 QUALITY ASSURANCE

Permits are required for the installation of all irrigation systems.

1.04 REFERENCES

NATIONAL ELECTRIC CODE, Current Edition
UNIFORM PLUMBING CODE, Current Edition

1.05 SUBMITTALS

A. AS-BUILT DRAWINGS

Contractor should furnish the Owner or Owner's representative with accurate, properly dimensioned, up-to-date drawings of any and all changes from the original plan that take place in the installation of the irrigation system.

B. OPERATION AND MAINTENANCE DATA

1. Contractor should furnish the Owner or Owner's representative with typed or printed instructions for the operation and maintenance of all irrigation equipment.

2. Contractor should furnish the Owner or Owner's representative with a copy of a controller schedule indicating water zone/station descriptions.

1.06 EXISTING CONDITIONS

Pavements should not be disturbed without the approval of the Owner or Owner's representative and then only in the event obstructions are encountered. Small test holes may be cut in the pavement to locate obstructions, with the approval of the Owner or Owner's representative.

1.07 SCHEDULING

Contractor should schedule the installation of necessary sleeving during the site preparation and hardscape operations.

1.08 SUBSTITUTIONS

All substitutions of materials should be of equal or greater quality and should be approved by the Owner or Owner's representative.

1.09 WARRANTY

Upon completion of the irrigation system installation, the Contractor should physically demonstrate to the Owner or Owner's representative how to set time controls, adjust sprinkler heads, and operate pumps and other equipment.

PART 2 — PRODUCTS

2.01 PIPE AND FITTINGS

A. RIGID PVC

Unless otherwise specified, all rigid plastic pipe should be polyvinyl chloride (PVC) and should conform to all requirements of product standards for PVC 1120, PVC 1220 (Type 1) or PVC 2120 (Type 2), National Sanitation Foundation (NSF) approved.

1. CONSTANT PRESSURE (MAIN LINE PIPE): All solvent weld joint piping subject to constant pressure within the system should be Class 315; Schedule 40 should be used for pipe sizes not exceeding 2 inches. Pipe 2-1/2 inches and larger should be Class 200 ring or gasket joint pipe with proper thrust blocking.

2. LATERAL PIPE: Piping downstream of the operating valves, not subject to constant pressure, should be a minimum of Class 200.

3. FITTINGS: All fittings for rigid PVC pipe should be either solvent weld, ring or gasket joint, gasketed compression, or IPS threaded type. Rigid plastic pipe should not be threaded. Heavy wall nipples Schedule 80 with molded threads are allowed.

   a. Solvent Weld: Fittings should be socket type PVC Schedule 40.

   b. Ring or Gasket Joint: Fittings should be of a type compatible with the pipe used and recommended for such application by the manufacturer.

   c. Compression: Fittings should be of a size and type compatible with PVC pipe, recommended by the manufacturer for such use, and pressure rated to meet or exceed the pressure requirements of the system.

   d. Threaded: All fittings for threaded valve assemblies should be threaded PVC Schedule 80.

4. THREADED NIPPLES: All nipples used for riser, swing joint, valve, or other threaded assemblies should be a minimum of Schedule 80 PVC with molded threads. Plain end pipe should not be threaded because of the notch-sensitive nature of PVC.

B. FLEXIBLE PE PLASTIC

1. PIPE: All flexible plastic pipe should be virgin polyethylene (PE) PE 2306, PE 3306, or PE 3406 Class 125 or greater, as required to meet or exceed the pressure requirements of the system.

2. FITTINGS: Fittings should be insert or compression type designed for use with PE pipe, recommended for that use by the manufacturer, and pressure rated to meet the system requirements.

C. GALVANIZED STEEL

1. PIPE: All steel pipe should be standard Schedule 40 galvanized steel pipe.

2. FITTINGS: Fittings should be standard malleable galvanized iron screwed pattern fittings.

3. NIPPLES: Threaded nipples should be standard Schedule 40 galvanized steel unless otherwise specified.

D. CAST IRON

1. PIPE: All pipe should be flanged or mechanically jointed type, a minimum of Class 150.

2. FITTINGS: Fittings should be standard flange or mechanical joint type compatible with the pipe and incorporating all required sealing gaskets.

E. COPPER

1. PIPE: Pipe should be Type L copper.

2. FITTINGS: Fittings should be standard solder type wrought copper or cast bronze, 150 psi.

2.02 BACKFLOW PREVENTION DEVICES
A. DESCRIPTION

Backflow prevention devices prevent backflow of contaminated water from the irrigation system into the domestic water supply.

1. Backflow can occur through any "cross-connection" between an irrigation system and a potable water system.

2. A cross-connection is any actual or potential connection in a water system where a potential contaminating material can come in contact with the potable water supply.

3. Backflow through a cross-connection in an irrigation system can occur in two ways:

   a. Backflow due to "backsiphonage" occurs when the supply pressure is interrupted and a negative pressure or siphon occurs, most commonly due to a greater demand elsewhere in the system.

   b. Backflow due to "backpressure" occurs when the downstream pressure exceeds the supply pressure due to pumping or pressure caused by elevation.

B. METHODS

1. Backflow prevention can be accomplished with an air gap, but is generally not practical in an irrigation system, since it requires a physical break in the supply piping and re-pumping for the irrigation system pressure.

2. Four types of backflow prevention devices can be used, depending on the application and local building code requirements.
    a. Atmospheric Vacuum Breaker
    b. Pressure Vacuum Breaker Assembly
    c. Double Check Valve Assembly
    d. Reduced Pressure Backflow Preventer

C. ATMOSPHERIC VACUUM BREAKER

1. DESCRIPTION AND OPERATION: Protects against backsiphonage by means of an air inlet, which is closed by a poppet when pressure is on the device. As pressure is relieved, the poppet moves off the inlet, allowing incoming air to break a siphon.

2. APPLICATION: Must not be subjected to continuous pressure more than 12 hours of every 24 hours or to possible backpressure due to pumping or elevation.

3. This section also applies to a separate anti-siphon device or a combination of an automatic or manual valve and an atmospheric vacuum breaker in one unit.

D. PRESSURE VACUUM BREAKER ASSEMBLY

1. DESCRIPTION AND OPERATION: Protects against backsiphonage by means of a check valve and an air inlet, which is closed when pressure is on the device. The poppet which closes the air inlet is spring loaded to assure that it opens even after being closed (pressurized) for long periods of time.

2. APPLICATION: Can be subjected to continuous pressure. Cannot be subjected to possible backpressure due to pumping or elevation.

3. TYPICAL APPLICATION: Protection for an entire irrigation system. Installed after the connection to the main (or meter) and before the manual or automatic sprinkler valves.

4. SPECIAL CONSIDERATIONS: Should not be installed where toxic fluids or fertilizers may backflow.

E. DOUBLE CHECK VALVE ASSEMBLY

1. DESCRIPTION AND OPERATION: Protects against backsiphonage and backpressure by means of two check valves in series, which prevent any backflow through the device.

2. APPLICATION: Can be subject to continuous pressure and to possible backpressure due to pumping or elevation. Cannot be installed where the potential backflowing material is hazardous, such as fertilizers or other chemicals.

3. TYPICAL APPLICATIONS: Protection for an entire irrigation system when chemical or fertilizer injection is not used. Installed after the connection to the main (or meter) and before the manual or automatic irrigation valves.

4. SPECIAL CONSIDERATIONS: This device is considered a "LOW HAZARD" device. Acceptance of double check valve assemblies on irrigation systems is most controversial. Consult local building code requirements before selecting this type of device.

F. REDUCED PRESSURE BACKFLOW PREVENTER

1. DESCRIPTION AND OPERATION: Protects against backsiphonage and backpressure by means of two check valves and a relief valve, which discharges the water from the "zone" between the check valves when a backflow occurs. The first check valve reduces the pressure, allowing the relief valve to "sense" a backflow condition due to a decrease in the inlet pressure (siphon) or an increase (backpressure) in the reverse direction against the downstream side of the device.

2. APPLICATION: Can be subjected to continuous pressure and to possible pressure due to pumping or elevation.

3. TYPICAL APPLICATIONS: Protection for an entire irrigation system, including systems where backpressure due to pumping or elevation could occur and where chemical or fertilizer injection occurs. Installed after the connection to the main (or meter) and before the manual or automatic sprinkler valves.

4. SPECIAL CONSIDERATIONS: This device is considered as "High Hazard" protection and generally may be installed where the potential backflowing material may be hazardous.

2.03 VALVES AND VALVE BOXES
A. QUICK COUPLER VALVES

Quick coupling (or snap) valves are similar to a hose bib but installed flush to grade with built-in valve. They require a special key to couple with and open the valve. Typically used with sprinkler attached to key or coupler or as hose outlet.

B. MANUAL VALVES: SPRINKLER, GLOBE, ANGLE, AND COMBINATION ANTI-SIPHON

Valves in this category stop and start flow and control pressure on sprinkler equipment downstream of its location.

C. MANUAL VALVES: MAIN SHUT-OFF OR GATE

This type of valve is used to control individual sections of irrigation systems for the purpose of repairs or modification. Its main requirement is that of low flow losses. Due to low cycling (opening and closing), maintainability is not as important as it is in sprinkler control valves.

D. CHECK VALVES: SPRING LOADED, HORIZONTAL OR VERTICAL

Check valves are installed for the purpose of allowing fluid flow in one direction while preventing flow in the opposite direction.

E. POWER VALVES: PRESSURE REDUCING AND PRESSURE SUSTAINING

These types of valves are installed to automatically maintain flow/pressure conditions downstream of their locations.

F. REMOTE CONTROL VALVES

Any device that can be opened and closed from a remote source to control the flow of irrigation water. Valves in this class are controlled remotely by an electrical or hydraulic signal and used to operate a series of sprinklers much the way a manually operated sprinkler valve functions. They are typically made of brass, cast iron, or plastic. Their controlling signal comes via a wire or hydraulic tube from a controller located at some convenient place on or off the site.

G. VALVE BOXES

Boxes specifically manufactured to house valves and prevent the valves from becoming buried in the surrounding soil. Valve boxes are made of concrete or plastic and are available in various sizes to house single or multiple valves.

2.04 CONTROLLERS AND CONTROL CIRCUITS

A. AUTOMATIC IRRIGATION CONTROLLERS

Any automatic timing device utilized to open and close remote control valves on a predetermined schedule for irrigation system programming, including:

1. Hydraulic

2. Electric operated by mechanical control knobs

3. Electric operated by electronic touch pad, includes memory with multiple functions

4. Electric combined with a radio signal

5. Solar powered

6. Hybrid controllers combining electronic timing and controls with mechanical input

B. LANDSCAPE IRRIGATION CONTROL CIRCUITS

Any electrical circuit that controls the operation of remote landscape irrigation equipment by supplying signals and/or power to a solenoid, thermal motor, clock motor, or equivalent actuating or control device.

C. CIRCUIT

Any combination of conductors used to transmit hydraulic or electrical energy.

D. CONTROLLER OUTPUT CIRCUITS

Output circuits must be inherently power-limited remote control circuits for signaling and/or actuating remote equipment used to control the operation of all or any portion of any type of landscape irrigation system.

1. The inherently limited power source for a landscape irrigation control circuit should be one of the following:

   a. A transformer approved for the purpose

   b. A primary battery

   c. Other inherently limited power source approved for this purpose and used in strict accordance with the terms of that approval.

2. Landscape irrigation control circuits should be supplied by an inherently limited power source capable of supplying not more than:

Circuit voltage- Vmax ....30 Volts
Volt amperes- VA....................100 VA
Current- I 100/Vmax
Current limitation- Imax ....5.0 Amps

Overcurrent protection: The inherently limited power sources specified above require no overcurrent protection.

E. CONDUCTORS

Any wire or cable suitable for carrying electrical current.

1. Conductors on the load (output) side of the limited power supply (transformer) should be no smaller than #14 if single conductor or #18 if multiple conductor for physical strength and should be

   a. UF cable, rated at 600 volts, per U/L Standard No. 493.

   b. Polyethlyene-insulated golf course and lawn sprinkler systems wire for direct burial, rated at 300 volts, per U/L Miscellaneous Wires.

   c. Other approved cable suitable for direct burial in the earth, which is rated at not less than 300 volts with a covering that is moisture-, fungus-, and sunlight-resistant and has a jacket (insulation) thickness of not less than 30 mils.

2. SPECIAL CONSIDERATIONS: Bell wire is not acceptable.

F. HYDRAULIC CONTROL TUBING

Any tubing capable of transmitting hydraulic pressure for the purpose of operating hydraulic remote control valves.

1. Tubing should be flexible PVC, polyethylene, or copper, with a minimum pressure rating of 200 psi in standard nominal sizes such as 1/4-inch O.D., with selection of sizing to be in strict accordance with the recommendations of the manufacturer of the control equipment as related to the type of equipment and the length of tubing.

2. Fittings should be standard solvent weld, barb or compression type, as recommended for the tubing used to maintain the 200 psi pressure rating of the control system.

3. Strainers of the proper type should be installed at the control system pressure connection, controller, and/or valves if so recommended by the manufacturer.

G. CONDUIT (SLEEVE)

A tube, pipe, or other enclosure through which electrical wires, hydraulic tubing, or pipes are run, to provide accessibility and protection from physical damage.

2.05 SPRINKLER HEADS, RISERS, AND ANTI-DRAIN VALVES
A. DEFINITIONS

1. ARC OF COVERAGE: The degree of coverage from one side of the throw of a sprinkler to the other. A half head has a 180 degree arc of coverage.

2. CAP: The top of a sprinkler, usually a pop-up type.

3. CASE: The exterior shell or body of a pop-up sprinkler.

4. CUT-OFF RISER: A nipple with several areas of threaded sections which can be cut off to reduce the height of the riser. Normally avoided in professional use.

5. FLEX RISER: A riser made of flexible material so that it can be bent without breaking. Usually used for mounting shrub or small lawn sprinklers, to avoid damage to the lateral piping.

6. FLUSHING ACTION: The method used to flush debris from around the nozzle assembly of pop-up sprinklers as they are either rising to operate or retracting after operation. Refers to water which bypasses the sprinkler riser seals before they seat.

7. POSITIVE RETRACTION: The feature of a pop-up sprinkler used to return it to the non-operating retracted position, usually by means of a spring.

8. RADIUS: The nominal distance water is thrown by a sprinkler.

B. SPRINKLER HEADS

The mechanism which is used to deliver water to the landscape.

1. BUBBLERS: A sprinkler which is used for small planters or individual plants. A bubbler is mounted above grade on a riser and distributes water in either a stream pattern or small fountain pattern.

2. FIXED SPRAY: A sprinkler in which the water delivery is continually being applied to the entire arc of coverage.

3. FLUSH HEAD: A sprinkler which is made for use in turf; without a pop-up feature. Normally avoided in professional use.

4. HI (OR HIGH) POP: A sprinkler which has a pop-up feature exceeding two inches. For use in taller turf installations or in ground cover and shrub areas.

5. POP-UP: A sprinkler which is usually used in turf areas; has a pop-up feature so it rises above the grass when in operation and retracts when not in operation.

6. ROTARY SPRINKLER: Cam driven, gear driven, impact or impulse driven; a sprinkler in which the water stream is rotated over the arc of coverage to attain greater distance, with a relatively low volume of water being used.

7. SHRUB HEAD: A sprinkler which is used in shrubbery or ground cover areas; does not have a pop-up feature.

8. STREAM SPRAY: A sprinkler in which water is channeled into streams in the sprinkler, but the streams are stationary and do not rotate over the arc of coverage.

C. RISERS

When used in describing a pop-up sprinkler, it is the stem to which the nozzle is affixed, which rises when the sprinkler is in operation. If referred to in conjunction with the mechanics of installing a sprinkler, it is the nipple on which the sprinkler head is mounted. Risers can be either Schedule 80 PVC, Marlex, poly, or galvanized steel.

D. SWING JOINTS AND FLEX RISERS

Provide protection to lateral pipes in areas where sprinkler heads are subject to impact.

1. SWING JOINTS: The joint between the lateral pipe and the riser on which a sprinkler is mounted. Single, double, and triple swing joints are fabricated from PVC, Marlex, galvanized steel, or a combination of fittings.

2. FLEX NIPPLES OR RISERS
   a. Manufactured flexible PVC hose with fixed threaded fittings on each end.
   b. Bulk Flexible PVC: Should be IPS (Iron Pipe Size) hose cut to desired length and solvent welded to PVC fittings, IPS hose should not be used on the pressure side of a valve.

E. ANTI-DRAIN VALVES

A valve used in sprinkler systems where elevation differences would cause a drainage of the sprinkler line through the lower sprinkler on the valve. Also referred to as a check valve. Some are adjustable. This valve will hold back a given head of water to eliminate low head drainage problems.

2.06 BOOSTER PUMPS

A. Used to increase existing pressure to a higher pressure at a given flow.

B. Booster pumps are typically centrifugal pumps driven by electric motors at 230/460 volts.

2.07 SOIL MOISTURE SENSING EQUIPMENT
A. APPLICATION

Provides an automatic override of the pre-programmed irrigation regimes, based on a continuous monitoring of soil moisture in relation to plant need. Manual instrumentation can also be employed which does not override the automatic controls but can be used to establish optimum programming/scheduling of irrigation.

B. TYPES

Two basic categories of moisture-sensing equipment are in general use:

1. TENSIOMETERS: Hollow, water-filled tubes with a ceramic sensing tip at one end and a hermetically sealed vacuum gauge at the other. Tube is sealed by means of a cap and stopper assembly. Measures soil suction (matric potential) on a direct basis.

2. ELECTRICAL RESISTANCE DEVICES: Use electrodes encased in a porous material (gypsum) to measure electrical resistance in the soil as an index to soil water. Data is calibrated for salinity, soil type, and temperature, and then converted into either soil suction or water content.

2.08 DRIP IRRIGATION COMPONENTS
A. VALVES

Manual or remote control valves used in drip irrigation applications must be designed to operate at minimal flow rates.

B. FILTRATION

Almost all drip irrigation systems require filtration. Mesh or micron requirements are recommended by most manufacturers.

1. MESH: Number of openings per lineal inch (a 40 mesh screen will pass particles up to .012 inch; a 100 mesh screen, particles up to .005 inch; and a 150 mesh screen particles up to .0037 inch).

2. MICRON: One millionth of a meter (2.54 micron= .001 inch, 127 micron .005 inch or 100 mesh screen).

C. TUBING

1. POLYETHYLENE: A relatively inexpensive and extremely flexible tubing that lends itself most readily to drip use. Quality of resins, amount of ultraviolet light inhibitor (normally carbon black) added, and extrusion technique can cause prices to vary greatly. Most reputable manufacturers will guarantee tubing for five or more years.

2. POLYPROPYLENE: Less flexible and normally more expensive than polyethylene but more resistant to high pressure and direct sunlight. Has more memory than polyethylene and tends to retain its coil shape.

3. POLYVINYL CHLORIDE (Flexible PVC): Heavier and more expensive than other drip tubing. Quality varies with resin quality and ultraviolet inhibitor. Not as resilient as other tubing and difficult to work with by comparison. Is less susceptible to mechanical damage and is used frequently when rodent damage is a problem.

4. All tubing must meet the following requirements:
   a. I.D. and O.D. must be published.
   b. Minimum carbon black percentage in polyethylene must be 2-1/2 %.
   c. Tubing must be of a material to prevent algae growth inside.
   d. Must take temperature extremes up to 140 degrees centigrade and water temperature to -40 degrees centigrade freezing.

D. FITTINGS

1. POLYETHYLENE TUBING
   a. Compression: Fittings that slide over the tubing and grip the outside. Various designs allow pressures up to 90 psi.
   b. Barbed Insert: Slips inside tubing to grip from the inside. For larger I.D. tubing (.375 inch and above), it should be used only for low pressures (3-25 psi). Creates stress cracks (longitudinal cracks along barbed area) in poor quality tubing exposed to sunlight.
   c. Barbed Insert with Lock Ring: Can be used at higher pressures than a barbed insert alone. Tends to leak when fastened in place and exposed to changes in temperature.

2. POLYPROPYLENE TUBING: Special compression fittings are required to hold the tubing in place or clamp over barbed insert fittings.

3. PVC TUBING: Solvent and regular Schedule 40 PVC fittings may be used. In some cases, special fittings are required by the manufacturer.

4. All fittings must meet the following requirements:
   a. Must specify tubing to be used by I.D. or O.D., depending on the type of tubing.
   b. Must withstand the design pressure of the system.
   c. Must meet the temperature extremes of up to 140 degrees centigrade water temperature to -40 degrees centigrade freezing.

E. EMISSION DEVICES
1. EMITTERS
   a. Compensating: Gives a fairly uniform flow through a predetermined pressure range. Used with low to medium pressure systems when changes in elevation create a differential throughout the system.
   b. Non-compensating: Does not compensate for pressure changes in the line.

2. MIST SPRAYERS: Small mist nozzles usually made of plastic to provide airborne moisture for humidity-loving plants. Also used for specialty planting, baskets, and special effects.

3. SOAKERS: Perforated or porous tubing developed to dispense water fairly evenly along the length of the tubing.
   a. Multi-chamber: Allows water to flow along the main channel and dispense through a lower pressure chamber or chambers. Spacing of outlets is commonly 6 to 24 inches.
   b. Single Chamber: Water flows along the tubing and is dispensed out holes along the chamber wall. Several variations are available, including emitters fitted inside the tubing and holes drilled at a shallow angle into the tubing by laser. Spacing of outlets is commonly 6 to 24 inches.
   c. Porous: Tubing extruded of a material that allows the entire tube to weep.

4. LOW-VOLUME SPRINKLERS: Miniature sprinklers in full and part circle patterns, used in ground cover areas where emitters or soakers are impractical.

5. All emission devices must meet the following requirements:
   a. All must have published flow rates at specific water pressures.
   b. Minimum and maximum operating pressure must be published.
   c. All devices must be self-purging or easily cleanable in the field.
   d. All emission devices must be capable of deterring the entrance and growth of insects.

2.09 OTHER IRRIGATION MATERIALS
The proper assembly of an irrigation system requires the use of other materials, including solvent cement, primer, joint sealant, teflon tape, copper solder and flux, and wire connectors. All such products should be used in strict accordance with the manufacturer's recommendations.

3.01 LAYOUT

The exact location of each sprinkler head, with proper spacing for even distribution of water, should be accurately determined and marked on the site to allow for proper routing of pipe and control wires, and proper location of control valves, backflow prevention, and the controller.

3.02 TRENCHING AND BACKFILLING
A. TRENCHING PROCEDURES

1. All trenches should be dug straight with vertical sides and with bottoms smooth and level. Trenches may be machine- or hand-dug; no plow type equipment should be permitted.

2. All trenches should be wide enough to permit easy access for installing pipe, wire, etc. and allow enough width for snaking of PVC pipe, to allow for expansion and contraction. Trench width should be a minimum of 2-1/2 times the size of the pipe.

3. All trenches should be dug to a depth to allow for 18 inches cover over main or pressure pipe and 12 inches cover over lateral or non-pressure pipe. In residential systems a minimum coverage of 12 inches is acceptable for main pipe and 8 inches for lateral pipe 1-1/2 to 1-1/4 inches in diameter.

B. DRILLING AND BORING

Conduit installed under existing pavement should be done by approved jacking or drilling methods. Jacking or drilling pits are to be kept at least two feet from pavement edge wherever possible. Excessive use of water that will soften sub-grade or undermine the pavement is not permitted. Water should be used only for cooling bit or removal of drilled material.

C. BACKFILL PROCEDURES

1. All lumber, rubbish, and rocks should be removed from trenches and backfill material, to ensure that the pipe will have a firm, uniform bearing for the entire length of each pipeline, to prevent uneven settlement.

2. In rocky areas the pipe should be laid on a minimum of four inches of sand and covered with four inches of sand to prevent rock damage to pipe.

3. Trenches should be backfilled with the excavated soil after pipe and wire have been installed and compacted by flooding to the same relative compaction as the surrounding soil.

4. The top six inches of backfill in planting areas should consist of selected excavated material, free of rocks, debris, vegetative material, and other undesirable material.

3.03 SLEEVING

Irrigation system piping under permanently paved areas such as, but not limited to, driveways, roads, parking lots, and walkways that exceed four feet in width should be installed within protective sleeving. Sleeving should be a minimum of Class 160 PVC or equivalent. Sleeving should be sized to allow an easy sliding fit of the irrigation pipe with fittings installed. Sleeving should have a minimum of eight inches of cover to the bottom surface of the paving and be installed at the depth of the piping, providing this requirement is met, and should extend a minimum of 12 inches beyond the outer edges of the paving.

EXCEPTION: On residential installations not subject to heavy traffic loads, sleeves may be installed with a minimum of four inches of cover to the bottom surface of the paving.

3.04 PIPE AND PIPE FITTINGS
A. HANDLING AND STORAGE

1. Due care should be exercised in the handling, loading, unloading, and storing of all pipe and fittings. Damaged pipe or fittings should not be installed in the irrigation system.

2. Pipe should be transported and stored on beds or pallets of sufficient length to allow pipe to lie flat. Avoid undue bending, stress, and concentrated external loads.

B. DEPTH OF COVER

1. MAIN PRESSURE LINES: All system piping subject to constant pressure should be installed with a minimum of 18 inches of cover (12 inches for residential systems) above the top of the pipe.

2. LATERAL AND FEEDER LINES: All system piping downstream of the operating valves should be installed with a minimum of 12 inches of cover (8 inches for residential systems) above the top of the pipe.

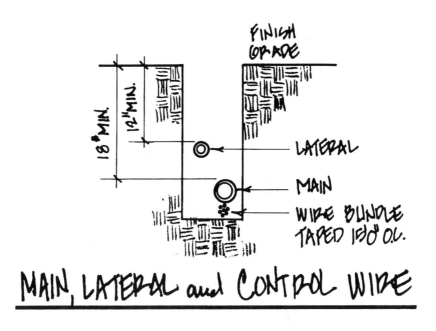

MAIN, LATERAL and CONTROL WIRE

C. PIPE PULLING

Plastic pipe up to 2 inches in size with a minimum wall thickness equivalent to Class 200 may be pulled into the ground to required depth with appropriate vibratory plow equipment. All other pipe should be installed in proper trenches.

D. PIPE INSTALLATION

1. PLASTIC PIPE: Solvent weld or insert fittings joined plastic pipe should be installed with moderate "snaking" from side to side in the trench to allow for expansion and contraction. Pipe should not be installed when air temperature is below 40 degrees Fahrenheit.

2. RING OR GASKET JOINT PIPE

   a. Pipe should not be deflected (curved) beyond the maximum joint deflection angle specified by the manufacturer.

   b. All ring or gasket joint pipe should be installed with proper thrust blocks at every change of direction of the pipe and every in-line valve.

E. THRUST BLOCKING

Thrust blocks should be concrete or similar permanent material, should bear upon solid undisturbed soil, and should be sized in accordance with the manufacturer's recommendations for adequate bearing surface to withstand the maximum surge pressure exerted against the soil type in which installed.

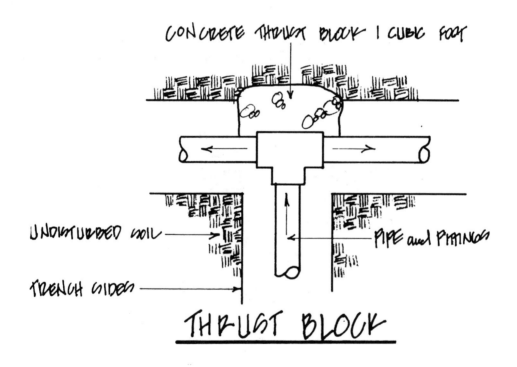

F. FABRICATION PROCEDURES

1. GENERAL: Care should be exercised during fabrication to avoid damage to pipe and fittings and to protect against the entry of dirt or other foreign material into the piping system during installation.

2. RIGID PLASTIC SOLVENT WELD JOINTS

   a. Pipe ends should be cut square, preferably with a wheel or vice type mechanical pipe cutter. All burrs and debris should be removed and pipe thoroughly cleaned and dried inside and out.

   b. Primer and solvent should be used in accordance with the manufacturer's recommendations with regard to all factors involved, such as pipe size and weather conditions.

   c. The entire bonding surfaces of the fittings and pipe should be properly coated with primer and solvent. Coating should be uniform and not excessive so as to force excess material into the pipe. Any external beads of excess material should be wiped clean from the joint.

   d. Pipe should be inserted firmly into the fitting to the shoulder, rotated approximately one-quarter turn to facilitate bonding and held in position against the fitting stop until set, to prevent pipe from backing out of the tapered fitting socket.

3. FLEXIBLE PLASTIC JOINTS: Manufacturer's instructions for the specific type and brand of fittings used should be carefully followed. Pipe ends should be cut square and pressed firmly to the fitting stops. See Drip Irrigation for drip applications.

4. GALVANIZED STEEL JOINTS: Pipe threads should be cleanly cut, free of all burrs and debris, and coated with an approved thread joint sealing compound prior to making up the joint.

5. CAST IRON JOINTS: All cast iron joints, flanged or mechanical, should be installed in strict accordance with the manufacturer's instructions and should include the proper sealing gaskets.

6. COPPER JOINTS: Copper pipe should be cut square with a wheel type cutter, cleaned, freed of all burrs or other extraneous materials, and treated with recommended flux before joining. Pipe should be inserted firmly to the fitting stop; fitting should be heated uniformly until solder is drawn completely into the joint and forms a uniform bead at the outer edge. All connections to threaded fittings or equipment should be made by using threaded adapters or fittings soldered to the pipe.

G. FLUSHING

All main and lateral lines should be thoroughly flushed before installing valves or sprinkler heads.

3.05   BACKFLOW PREVENTION DEVICES
A.   GENERAL INSTALLATION REQUIREMENTS

1. LOCATION: Whenever practical, the device should be installed so that it is hidden or partially hidden by landscape material or a physical structure.

2. PROPER HEIGHT OF INSTALLATION: Devices should not be installed at an extreme height which is impractical for proper accessibility for testing or maintenance.

3. PROPER POSITIONING: Devices must be installed in proper positions (as recommended by the manufacturer) so that proper function of air inlets and relief valves is assured. Piping must be rigid and vertical or horizontal as required.

4. OBSTRUCTION OF TEST COCKS: All devices must be installed in such a manner that all test cocks are readily accessible for testing procedures.

5. FREEZING PROTECTION: Must be provided where needed without interfering with the air inlets or relief valve discharge.

B.   ATMOSPHERIC VACUUM BREAKER

1. Must be installed above ground at least six inches above the highest outlet and per local building code requirements.

2. Must be installed with rigid piping, galvanized steel, or SCH 80 PVC minimum.

3. Must be installed on the downstream side of the valve.

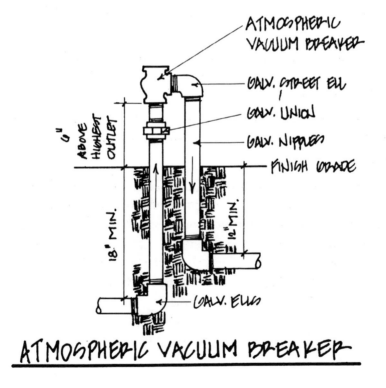

ATMOSPHERIC VACUUM BREAKER

C.   PRESSURE VACUUM BREAKER ASSEMBLY

1. Must be installed above ground at least 12 inches above the highest outlet.

2. Must be installed with galvanized steel or rigid copper piping.

3. Must be positioned properly so the piping in and out of the device is vertical.

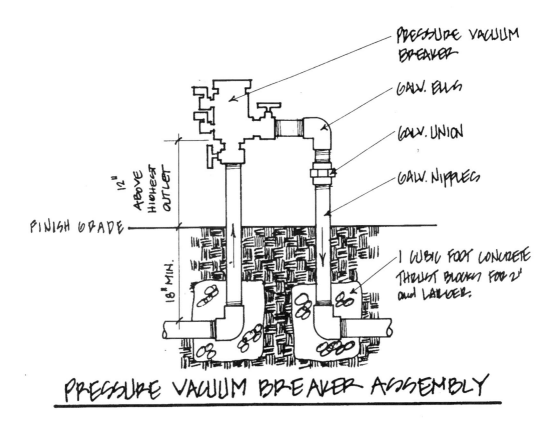

PRESSURE VACUUM BREAKER ASSEMBLY

D. DOUBLE CHECK VALVE ASSEMBLY

1. Should be installed above ground to facilitate testing and maintenance. Minimum height is 12 inches. Maximum height is 30 inches.

2. Must be installed with galvanized steel or rigid copper piping.

3. Devices 2-1/2 inches and larger should be installed with at least one support saddle under the device to eliminate stress on the piping or device (refer to manufacturer's recommendations).

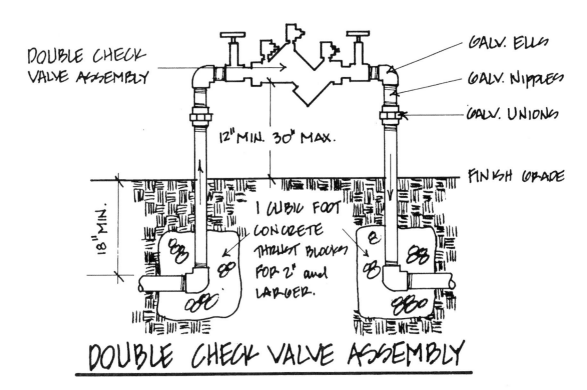

DOUBLE CHECK VALVE ASSEMBLY

93

E. REDUCED PRESSURE BACKFLOW PREVENTOR

1. Must be installed above ground level to allow for complete drainage of water flowing from relief valve. A minimum of 12 inches is recommended between the relief valve port and ground or floor level.

2. Must be installed and located so that it is readily accessible for periodic testing and maintenance.

3. Must be installed with galvanized steel or rigid copper piping.

4. Devices 2-1/2 inches and larger should be installed with at least one support saddle under the device to eliminate stress on the piping or device (refer to manufacturer's recommendations).

5. BASEMENT INSTALLATION: May be installed in a basement only if an adequate floor drain is provided to drain off all potential relief valve drainage. The device should be installed with the relief valve port a minimum of 12 inches above the floor.

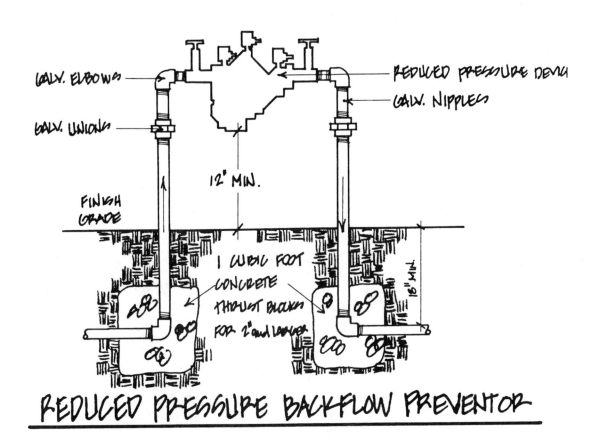

REDUCED PRESSURE BACKFLOW PREVENTOR

3.06   VALVES AND VALVE BOXES
A.   QUICK COUPLER VALVES

1. LOCATION: Should be installed off turf areas, where possible, in shrub or ground cover areas, or in rough unplanted areas.

2. DEPTH/HEIGHT

   a. Cover should be flush with grade in turf areas. A rubber cover should be used in turf play areas.

   b. May be elevated above ground cover or shrubs for ease in locating and for accessibility.

   c. Should be elevated two inches above surface in dirt areas.

3. PLUMBING AND INSTALLATION

   a. Tee on main line should be threaded and installed on its side.

   b. Offset nipples in riser assembly should be SCH 80 PVC with approved mates or SCH 40 galvanized steel waterproofed to prevent corrosion.

   c. Minimum length on vertical nipple should be 3 to 4 inches.

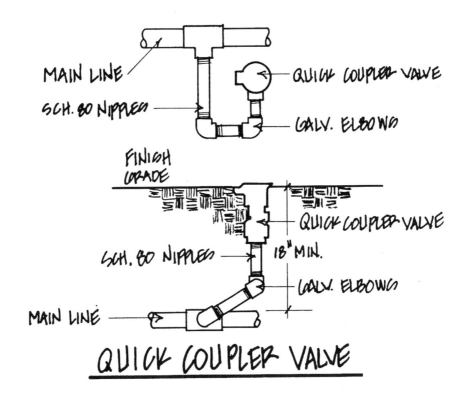

QUICK COUPLER VALVE

95

B. MANUAL VALVES: SPRINKLER, GLOBE, ANGLE AND COMBINATION ANTI-SIPHON

1. LOCATION: Should be installed adjacent to hard-surfaced areas in an area convenient to user/operator, out of range of the sprinklers being controlled.

2. DEPTH/HEIGHT

   a. Combination anti-siphon valves must be installed a sufficient height above the highest sprinkler head it serves to meet local building code requirements (usually six inches).

   b. Non-anti-backflow valves should be installed at main/lateral depths.

3. PLUMBING AND INSTALLATION

   a. Materials: Should be SCH 40 galvanized steel nipples and fittings or SCH 80 PVC pipe and fittings.

   b. When manifolded (multiple valves in one location), valves should be separated from adjacent valves by nipples of sufficient length (5 inches) to permit removal without interference with adjacent valve. Unions should be installed to facilitate repairs when galvanized steel pipe and fittings are used.

   c. Flush mounted valves (non anti-siphon types) should be provided with sleeves or collars sufficient to extend two inches above grade in shrub areas or flush with grade in areas where mowing is required. These sleeves should be a minimum of 6 inches in diameter for hand-operated valves and should be provided with covers. Sleeves can be 3 inches in diameter for key-operated valve with cross handle.

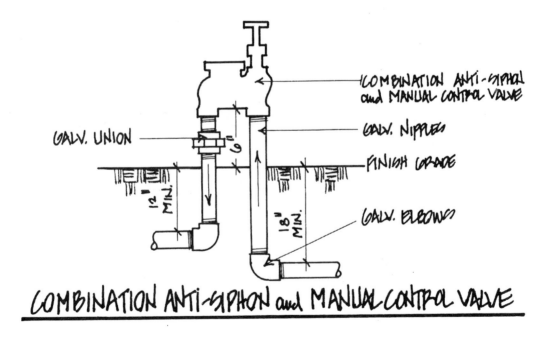

COMBINATION ANTI-SIPHON and MANUAL CONTROL VALVE

C. MANUAL VALVES: MAIN SHUT-OFF AND GATE VALVES

1. LOCATION: Minimum of one required, located at the point of connection to the water supply pipe. Exception: When the backflow prevention device or a master electric control valve is installed at the point of connection, a main shut-off valve is not required.

2. DEPTH/HEIGHT: Should be installed at depth of main line.

3. PLUMBING AND INSTALLATION

   a. Install in a valve box, with extensions if required, and set cover two inches above final grade.

   b. On nut-operated gate valve, provide at least one wrench of sufficient length to extend three feet above grade while resting in operating position on valve.

4. IDENTIFICATION: Main line shut-offs should be labeled with non-deteriorating tags corresponding to designations on the irrigation plans or on valve box cover.

D. CHECK VALVES: HORIZONTAL, VERTICAL, AND SPRING LOADED

1. LOCATION: Should be at the point of connection to the water supply pip immediately upstream from the water meter, or as specified.

2. DEPTH/HEIGHT: May be installed above or below ground, as required.

3. PLUMBING AND INSTALLATION

   a. Check valves which are to be located below grade should be enclosed in a non-deteriorating box of sufficient size to provide easy access for repair purposes.

   b. Where installed in a valve box, provide six inches of pea gravel under valve, for drainage purposes.

   c. Where check valve is 2-1/2 inches or larger, unions or flanged connections should be provided for repair/replacement purposes, and support or bearing blocks installed.

4. IDENTIFICATION: Where box and cover are located below grade, dimensions to existing permanent on-site points should be provided on as-built drawings.

E. POWER VALVES: PRESSURE REDUCING AND PRESSURE SUSTAINING

1. LOCATION: Where possible, locate above grade and under cover.

2. DEPTH/HEIGHT: May be installed above or below ground, per local building code requirements.

3. PLUMBING AND INSTALLATION

   a. Provide unions or flanged connections for ease in repair/replacement.

   b. Provide support or bearing block under all valves 2-1/2-inches or larger. These supports should be of concrete or steel.

   c. Where below grade, install in valve box of sufficient size to allow easy access for adjusting, repair, or replacement. Provide six inches pea gravel under valve(s) for drainage purposes.

4. IDENTIFICATION: Provide plastic or metal tag affixed to valve, showing proper pressure/flow adjustment settings.

F. REMOTE CONTROL VALVES

1. LOCATION

   a. Valves should not be located in turf areas, where possible.

   b. When located in turf areas, valve box should be flush with finish grade; or if below grade, location should be marked with valve marker.

   c. Valve should be located outside sprinkler coverage of heads being controlled, where possible.

2. DEPTH/HEIGHT

   a. Valve lateral top of pipe should be a minimum of inches below finish grade.

   b. No valve lateral top of pipe should be below 20 inches of finish grade.

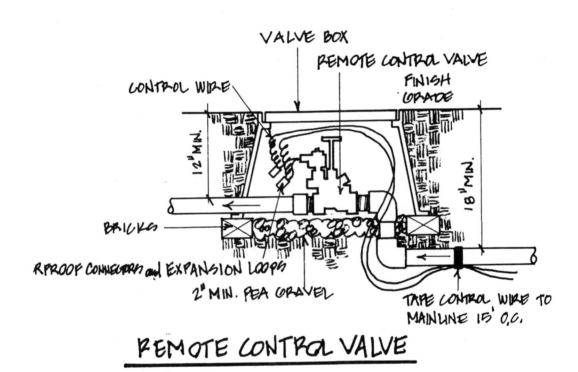

REMOTE CONTROL VALVE

3. PLUMBING AND INSTALLATION

   a. All valves should be installed within a valve box. No direct burials should be allowed.

   b. Each valve should have a minimum of two inches horizontal clearance from any enclosing valve box, adjacent valve, or other obstruction.

   c. All valves should have unlimited vertical clearance with valve cover open. A minimum of two inches vertical clearance should exist from highest point on valve to lowest point on cover.

   d. No more than one valve should be installed in a valve box unless proper clearance as stated above can be maintained.

e. All valves should be equipped with a flow control mechanism if the system pressure could result in excessive pressure reaching the sprinkler heads. Excessive pressure is defined as being that pressure over and above the manufacturer's catalogued pressure for that model and nozzle combination and approved for that application.

f. Piping from adjacent valves should have a minimum of two inches horizontal clearance at all points.

g. Where valves are to be manifolded, use SCH 40 galvanized nipples and fittings, SCH 80 PVC threaded nipples and fittings, or SCH 40 PVC pipe and solvent fittings, solvent welded according to manufacturer's specifications.

4. IDENTIFICATION: Each valve should be provided with an embossed plastic or metal tag showing the controller and station number controlling said valve.

G. VALVE BOXES

1. Rectangular valve boxes should be supported by four, non-deteriorating blocks on each of the four corners, placed on solid, undisturbed soil. Round, individual boxes should be shored with solid material.

2. No part of valve box or shoring should bear on the main, lateral piping or valve bodies and/or appurtenances.

3. The bottom of valve box should be covered with up to four inches of pea gravel to within two inches of parting line between valve body and cover or bonnet, to provide adequate drainage.

3.07 CONTROLLERS AND CONTROL CIRCUITS
A. LOCATION

1. OUTDOOR HOUSING: Any controller with a weather-resistant housing designated by the manufacturer, as suitable for outdoor installation, may be installed in an outdoor location, even if exposed to the natural elements, but should be located where it is not exposed to direct heavy spray from nearby sprinklers, or may be protected by suitable means from such direct spray.

2. INDOOR HOUSING: Any controller not specifically designated by the manufacturer as having weather-resistant housing suitable for outdoor installation shall be installed only in an indoor location or other completely waterproof housing device where it is fully protected from moisture and direct exposure to the elements.

3. PLUG-IN TRANSFORMER: Any controller utilizing a plug-in transformer as its source of power, regardless of housing designation, is considered to be an indoor controller, and the transformer shall be inserted only into an electrical outlet in a fully protected location. In no case should a plug-in transformer be allowed in an outdoor outlet, even if designated as a weatherproof outlet, since the opened cover required for insertion of the transformer destroys the weatherproof condition of the outlet. The transformer should be securely fastened into an indoor outlet on an unswitched circuit.

B. CONTROLLER INSTALLATION

1. WALL-MOUNTED HOUSING: Any controller in a housing designed for mounting on a vertical wall, whether indoor or outdoor, should be securely mounted to the wall in strict accordance with the manufacturer's mounting instructions. Outdoor models should be installed at least 36 inches high above a hard-surfaced area, where they are operationally accessible and where the operator is protected from irrigation spray.

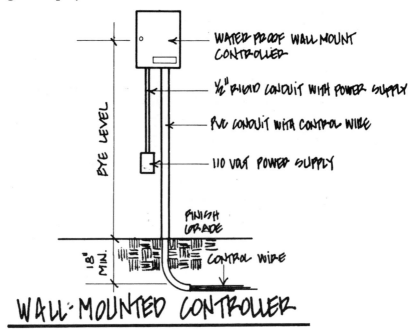

WALL-MOUNTED CONTROLLER

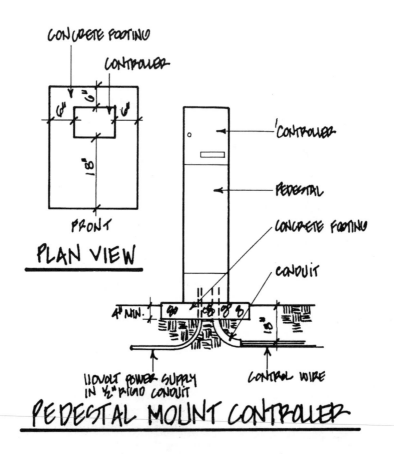

PLAN VIEW

PEDESTAL MOUNT CONTROLLER

2. PEDESTAL TYPE HOUSING: Any controller with weather-resistant housing designated by the manufacturer as suitable for outdoor installation that is designed for pedestal type mounting should have the pedestal standard secured firmly to an appropriate concrete base in strict accordance with the manufacturer's installation instructions.

C. CONTROLLER POWER SUPPLY

1. OUTDOOR INSTALLATION: The permanent installation of a 120 volt, 60 hertz power supply to an outdoor controller should be performed under a suitable permit in strict compliance with local electrical codes and by personnel properly trained in such installations. If an underground power supply is required, conduit specifications and depth of cover should comply with local code requirements. The National Electrical Code, Article 300, Section 300-5, requires for circuits of 0-600 volts, nominal, direct burial Type UF cable minimum cover of 24 inches, rigid metal conduit minimum cover of 6 inches, and PVC conduit minimum cover of 18 inches. EXCEPTION NO. 4 of Article 300-5: Residential branch circuits rated 300 volts or less and provided with overcurrent protection of not more than 30 amperes shall be permitted with a cover requirement of 12 inches. Direct buried conduit and cables emerging from the ground shall be protected in rigid metal conduit or Schedule 80 rigid non-metallic conduit, extending from the minimum cover distance required to the junction box. All underground installations shall be grounded and bonded in accordance with Article 250 of the National Electric Code. It is recommended that no taps or splices be made in underground power conductors even if allowed by the governing code.

2. INDOOR INSTALLATION: The permanent installation of a 120 volt, 60 hertz power supply to an indoor controller should be performed with a suitable permit in strict compliance with local electrical codes and by personnel properly trained in such installations. All power supply conductors should be in approved conduit. Power must be from a continuous unswitched circuit.

   An isolation switch or hand-operable circuit breaker may be installed near the controller to turn off power for purposes of service and/or maintenance, provided that such devices are placed in an approved enclosure with a door or cover plate to prevent inadvertent switching of the controller power supply.

3. PLUG-IN TRANSFORMER: Any controller that obtains its power through a plug-in transformer is considered to be a polyconnected appliance. The transformer can be plugged directly into any standard 120 volt, 60 hertz overcurrent protection electrical outlet that is weather protected and not subject to water or moisture contact or exposure. The plug-in connection must be direct and secured. The use of extension cords is not allowed.

D. DIRECT BURIAL CONDUCTOR INSTALLATION

1. MINIMUM COVER REQUIREMENTS: Conductors for power-limited irrigation control circuits as defined herein and installed with approved cable should be installed in the same trenches and at the same depth as the irrigation system main line piping wherever feasible. Conductors not installed with system piping should have a minimum cover of 6 inches if within conduit or 12 inches if direct burial.

2. BURIAL UNDER PAVING: Conductors under paving should be enclosed within suitable conduit or pipe sleeve, with sweep ells at each change of direction under the paving.

3. SPLICES AND TAPS: Splices and taps of underground conductors should be made only within splice boxes, valve boxes, or other suitable enclosures that provide access for inspection and/or repair. Splices or taps should be made by a competent technician using materials approved for the purpose and following the manufacturer's recommended procedures. Conductors should be joined by soldering or approved solderless mechanical connectors, either of which must be fully insulated and sealed against moisture.

4. SINGLE CONDUCTORS: All conductors of the same control circuit should be installed in the same trench and be run consistently along the same side of the irrigation system piping wherever feasible.

5. CONDUCTOR HANDLING: Conductors should be handled with all due care during installation to avoid any damage to the wire or insulation. Any conductor broken outside a splice box or enclosure should be replaced between splice boxes. Any damaged insulation must be immediately repaired with two to three layers of approved electrical tape extending beyond the limits of the damage, then thoroughly coated with approved waterproof external coating materials.

6. BUNDLING AND EXPANSION COILS: Multiple direct burial conductors in the same trench should be bundled and wrapped together with electrical tape or other suitable permanent fasteners at intervals of not more than 15 feet. Expansion coils consisting of not less than five turns of wire around a minimum 1-inch pipe, which is then withdrawn, should be installed at all valves, abrupt turns in direction of the wire, and in straight runs at intervals of not more than 100 feet.

7. CABLE CODING: Direct burial cables for the common conductor and for independent signal or other special circuits other than valve actuating conductors should be individually identified by color coding or other distinctive permanent marking on the exterior surface for their entire length. Where multiple controllers are used, controllers shall have individual letter designations (A, B, C, etc.), and different tracer colors should be used to identify the white common and/or other special circuit conductors for each separate controller circuit.

8. CONDUCTOR TERMINATION AT EQUIPMENT: Direct burial conductors terminating in connections to remote control valves or other control equipment will be permitted with less than the minimum cover requirement if the conductor rises vertically to the connection within a suitable protective enclosure.

E. ABOVE GROUND CONDUCTOR INSTALLATION
1. PROTECTION
   a. Direct burial conductors brought above ground for connection to the limited power source or for other purposes should be protected within a suitable conduit, raceway, or enclosure from below grade at the depth of the minimum cover requirement to the equipment enclosure.
   b. Conductors for the landscape irrigation control circuits should not be placed in the same conduit, raceway, junction box, or conduit body with conductors of light, power, or Class I circuits.

c. Conductors of two or more landscape irrigation control circuits are permitted within the same conduit, raceway, junction box, or conduit body.

2. SPECIAL LEADS: Single conductors on the load (output) side of the controller's inherently limited power source are permitted in sizes of No. 16 and/or No. 18 for terminal connections and pigtail leads no longer than 72 inches to be enclosed in conduit to a splice point to the larger conductors within standard junction boxes or conduit bodies of adequate size which are rigidly secured.

F.   HYDRAULIC CONTROL TUBING

1. A three-way valve or a shut-off valve and drain valve combination should be installed at or near the pressure connection, to provide future service and/or drainage of the control system.

2. The pressure connection to the system main line should be made upstream of the main shut-off valve and the first remote control valve.

3. Adaption of tubing size, if necessary, should be made at the controller and valve connections in accordance with the manufacturer's recommendations.

4. The discharge tube should be installed in a manner that will protect it from physical damage and allow discharge to atmosphere at least six inches above ground level in an acceptable location.

5. Tubing should be installed in the same trench and at the same depth as the main system piping, placed consistently on the same side of the piping wherever feasible, and taped or otherwise securely bundled at intervals of not more than 10 feet. Where tubing cannot be installed with the system piping, a minimum cover of 12 inches should be maintained.

6. Tubing should be installed loosely in the trench, with moderate snaking to allow for expansion and contraction, and should not be pulled taut.

7. An expansion coil consisting of a loop of tubing not less than 12 inches in diameter should be provided at each valve, the pressure connection, and each 90-degree change of direction, to allow for expansion and contraction, prevent strain on connections, and facilitate future service.

3.08   SPRINKLER HEADS, RISERS, AND ANTI-DRAIN VALVES
A.   TURF SPRINKLERS

1. LOCATION: The location of the sprinklers should be in general conformance with the irrigation system design, with distance between sprinklers not to exceed manufacturer's recommendations for a 3-5 mph wind condition. Sprinklers should be installed no closer than two inches from hard surface edges and lawn edges, to provide sufficient room for edgers to be used without damaging the sprinklers.

2. TYPE OF SPRINKLER: It is recommended that all turf sprinklers be of the popup variety with spring retraction.

3. CAP HEIGHT: The cap of pop-up sprinklers, mounted in turf areas, should be at grade level, to avoid damage from lawn mowers. There should be no depression around the sprinkler, and the sprinkler should not be mounted so the cap is below grade. This will prevent backwash of dirt in the bowl of the sprinkler and puddling of water over the sprinkler.

4. RISERS: Risers can be either SCH 80 PVC, Marlex, poly, or galvanized steel. It is recommended not to use SCH 40 PVC pipe with male or female adapters solvent welded to it, or non-flex cut-off risers.

5. LATERAL PROTECTION: The use of a swing joint or flex riser is recommended, to provide protection to the lateral piping.

6. INSTALLATION PROCEDURES: Before mounting sprinklers on risers, the lateral line should be flushed out with water from the valve to get rid of dirt, debris, or pipe chips and eliminate the problem of clogging nozzles. Many sprinklers have detachable nozzles so the head can be mounted and flushing can be done through the head before the nozzle is attached.

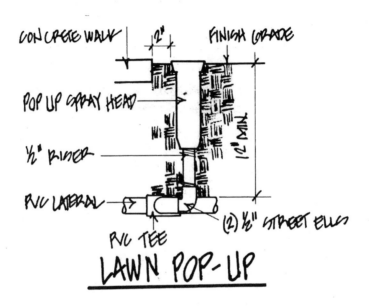

LAWN POP-UP

B. SHRUB SPRINKLERS

1. LOCATION: The location of the shrub sprinkler should be in general conformance with the irrigation system design, with distance between sprinklers not to exceed manufacturer's recommendations for a 3-5 mph wind condition. It is recommended that shrub sprinklers be placed between shrubbery and a building so they throw away from the building. Conditions sometime prevent this. However, every effort should be made to keep the shrub sprinklers from throwing onto the building. This also applies to walls and fences.

2. TYPE OF SPRINKLER: All types of sprinklers can be used in shrub and ground cover installations, as a sprinkler protruding above the plant material is considered acceptable as long as it does not constitute a safety hazard. In situations where sidewalks or driveways abut the ground cover or shrub areas, high-pop sprinklers should be used adjacent to pavements to avoid a safety hazard. This will also prevent damage to the sprinkler and the lateral line. If impact or impulse sprinklers are used in ground cover or shrub areas bordering walks or streets, the sprinkler should have an anti-back-splash feature to prevent a safety hazard and waste of water.

3. HEIGHT: Shrub sprinklers should be mounted at a height so that the waterthrow will not be interrupted by the plant materials. Care should be taken that elevated shrub sprinklers do not cause an infraction of the local code in regard to the height of the backflow prevention device.

4. RISERS: When shrub sprinklers are mounted above grade, poly or Marlex risers should not be used, nor PVC pipe solvent be welded to male or female adapters. Threaded SCH 80 PVC risers or galvanized steel risers are the only acceptable risers to be used above ground.

5. LATERAL PROTECTION: When shrub sprinklers are mounted above grade, they are subject to being hit by objects or pedestrians. To protect the lateral piping from being broken in such a situation, a flexible interface between the above ground riser and the lateral piping should be used. This can be accomplished by use of a flexible riser or a swing joint below ground. An alternate is the use of rebar or channel iron as a stake to make the riser inflexible.

6. INSTALLATION PROCEDURE: Before installing sprinklers on risers, the lateral lines should be flushed with water from the valve to get rid of dirt, debris, and pipe chips and eliminate the problem of clogging nozzles.

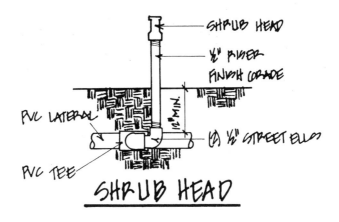

C. BUBBLER SPRINKLERS

1. LOCATION: The location of the bubblers should be in general conformance with the irrigation system design. As bubblers are normally used for small planters or individual plants, location of the bubblers should be determined by plant location.

2. CAP HEIGHT: Bubblers should be mounted above grade but kept low so they do not distract from the landscaping. Usually three inches above grade is sufficient. Care should be taken that elevated bubblers do not cause an infraction of the local code in regard to the height of the backflow prevention device.

3. RISERS: Bubblers should be installed on SCH 80 PVC or galvanized steel risers.

4. LATERAL PROTECTION: Should be provided the same as for shrub sprinklers.

5. INSTALLATION PROCEDURES: Before installing bubblers on risers, the lateral lines should be flushed with water from the valve to get rid of dirt, debris, and pipe chips and eliminate the problem of clogging nozzles.

D. SWING JOINTS AND FLEX RISERS

1. USE OF SWING JOINTS: Swing joints are generally used for shrub and bubbler sprinklers since these sprinklers can be susceptible to external impact. They are also often used on pop-up sprinklers in turf areas where the turf borders driveways or streets where vehicles could run over the turf sprinklers or in large turf areas where heavy maintenance equipment could run over the sprinklers (such as parks, cemeteries, golf courses, and athletic fields).

2. SWING JOINT MAKE-UP: If Marlex street ells are used, no special installation procedures have to be taken. If PVC or galvanized fittings are used, teflon tape or paste must be applied on all threads to keep the threads mobile.

3. SINGLE SWING JOINTS: Single swing joints should originate from the threaded outlet of a lateral fitting (either tee or ell), with the outlet being parallel to the grade. Although not the only accepted fitting to use in a swing joint, Marlex street ells, t x t are recommended. On a single swing joint, a t x t street ell or a t x t standard ell with a TBE short nipple should be used. This gives rotational ability in one direction. Theory is that any pressure to the other plane would allow the lateral pipe to "roll" rather than snap.

4. DOUBLE SWING JOINT: A double swing joint begins the same as the single swing, but with the addition of a single t x t ell (street ell or standard ell with t x t nipple). The double swing joint allows mobility in planes above ground, relieving stress on the lateral piping.

5. TRIPLE SWING JOINT: The addition of a third t x t ell gives the triple swing joint the added ability to allow the sprinkler to be raised or lowered while remaining perpendicular to the grade. Although three street ells will allow the triple swing, the up and down limits are severely restricted so it is recommended that a long nipple is added prior to the last ell to allow more vertical flexibility.

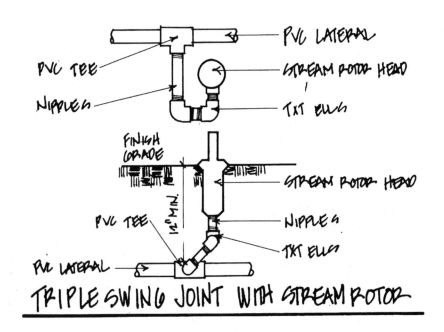

TRIPLE SWING JOINT WITH STREAM ROTOR

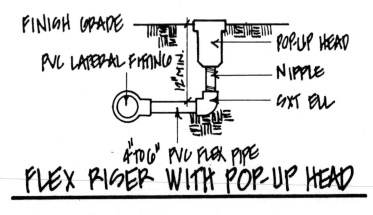

FLEX RISER WITH POP-UP HEAD

6. FLEX RISERS: In many instances, flex risers may be used in place of swing joints on sprinkler heads using 1/2- and 3/4-inch risers.

E. STAKING

Rebar or channel iron should be used for staking. Stake should extend a minimum of four inches below the trench bottom and should be banded to the riser with stainless steel clamps in at least two points no closer than 12 inches apart. CAUTION: Staked risers can be hazardous in areas of pedestrian traffic; the use of 6- or 12-inch hi-pop shrub sprinkler heads is recommended in these areas.

F. ANTI-DRAIN VALVES

1. LOCATION: Anti-drain valves are usually located between the lateral line and the sprinkler, below ground, or within the height of the shrubbery. The anti-drain valves should be installed on the lower sprinklers in a given section to prevent low head drainage. Depending on the manufacturer, anti-drain valves can hold back water under as much as a 12-foot head (12-foot high column of water).

2. TYPES: Anti-drain valves can be either pressure-fixed or adjustable and have threaded inlets and outlets.

3. USE OF CHECK VALVE IN PLACE OF ANTI-DRAIN VALVE: If a check valve is used in lieu of an anti-drain valve, it is only effective in holding water in a line going up in elevation and is usually used in the lateral line rather than in the riser to which a sprinkler is mounted. A check valve will hold back a much higher head of water than an anti-drain valve. The location of the check valve should be at a location just downstream of a sprinkler which would normally be subject to low head drainage due to the lateral line being higher than that particular sprinkler head. If there are other lower sprinkler heads, other check valves will have to be placed in the line, to prevent water in the lateral between the first check valve and the upstream but lower sprinklers from draining out those sprinklers.

3.09 BOOSTER PUMPS

A. GENERAL REQUIREMENTS

1. Booster pumps should be installed on a solid, level base of either concrete or steel. Mounting fasteners to hold pump vibration free should be included in base preparation.

2. Electric connections should be in accordance with local codes and they should be watertight and in rigid conduit.

3. The booster pump inlet should be under positive pressure.

B. INSTALLATION

1. Booster pump installation should include:

   a. A low-intake water circuit to shut down the pump if the intake water supply is interrupted or falls to a low level.

   b. A low-discharge pressure safety circuit to shut down the pump if the discharge pressure drops to a predetermined level due to a line break.

c. A high-discharge pressure safety circuit to shut down the pump if the discharge pressure reaches a predetermined high level.

d. A check valve to eliminate backsiphonage should be used if elevation differences warrant it.

e. A reduced pressure principal backflow device must be used to protect a potable water supply that is the common source of supply of an irrigation system using a booster pump.

2. Booster pumps installed outdoors should have waterproof electric motors or a water protection structure.

3.10 SOIL MOISTURE SENSING EQUIPMENT

A. LOCATION

1. Moisture sensors should be located in areas typical of that being controlled. Consideration should be given to the topography, sun and wind exposure, soil type, and type of plant materials.

2. In general, moisture sensors should be installed in areas that tend to become drier more frequently. Avoid installing the moisture sensors in bare spots, drainage areas, or areas which tend to be excessively wet.

B. METHODS OF CONTROL

1. AUTOMATIC OPERATION: Can be accomplished by controlling individual valves, groups of valves, or the entire controller. Method of control depends on the type of controller being used. (Certain controllers have built-in moisture-sensing terminals for the entire program or individual programs.)

2. MANUAL OVERRIDE: A manual override switch should be provided to eliminate moisture sensors from automatic operations.

3. WIRING: Wiring of moisture sensors can vary greatly, depending on controller specified and the type of control necessary. Follow manufacturer's recommended procedures.

4. MANUAL INSTRUMENTATION: Can be accomplished by periodically taking readings from instrument gauges and using them as guidelines to program or start up irrigation on an automatic or manual irrigation system.

C. INSTALLATION

1. HOUSING ENCLOSURES: All moisture sensors should be installed in appropriately protective enclosures and marked to facilitate finding them for future servicing.

2. DRAINAGE: All moisture sensor enclosures should have adequate drainage 'in the bottom to provide for escape of any water trapped inside the enclosure.

3. WIRE AND WIRE SPLICES: All wire splices should be electrically sound and waterproof.

4. EXPANSION LEADS: Additional footage of control wire expansion lead should be provided at each moisture-sensing location to facilitate servicing.

5. WIRE SIZE: Must be AWG-UF #14 or larger.

6. SENSING TIPS: Should be installed directly in the active root system of the plant material being monitored. Tensiometers have two moisture sensors; one should be located in the "shallow" root system and one in the "deeper" root system.

7. PROCEDURES: All installation, calibration, controller programming, periodic maintenance, and wiring should be done according to the manufacturer's specifications.

3.11 DRIP IRRIGATION

A. DESCRIPTION

Low-volume irrigation designed to water specific plants or plant areas with specific flow rates controlled by emission devices. Water is normally transmitted to those devices through flexible poly tubing and, depending upon the equipment used, the pressure can range from 3 to 90 psi.

B. APPLICATION

Drip irrigation can be utilized in exterior and interior landscapes for trees and shrubs; planter boxes, pots and other confined areas; sculptures, living walls and other living special effects; and all other planted areas that require specific watering, including exhibition areas, flower and vegetable gardens, and greenhouses. The use of drip irrigation in turf areas is limited to soaker applications buried in the turf.

C. BACKFLOW REQUIREMENTS

All drip systems connected to potable (drinking) water systems must be protected against backflow of irrigation water.

D. PRESSURE RANGES

1. LOW PRESSURE (3-25 psi): This pressure range is used when adapting products designed for agriculture to landscape use. a. Pressure regulation or flow restriction devices are required. b. Filtration of 150 mesh or better is normally required. c. Caution: With elevation changes, pressure decreases .433 psi per foot of elevation increase.

2. MEDIUM PRESSURE (15-45 psi)

   a. Pressure regulation or flow restriction devices are normally required.

   b. Filtration of 150 mesh or better is normally required.

3. HIGH PRESSURE (30-90 psi): This equipment is normally designed specifically for landscape use.

   a. Filtration of 80 mesh is normally required.

   b. Changes in elevation have less significant effects on flow rates or non-compensating devices.

   c. Pressure regulation is required over 90 psi.

E. SYSTEM PLANNING

1. All systems should be designed with ease of maintenance and future flexibility in mind.

2. The total amount of water required for each plant in landscape area should be determined.

3. The system should be laid out over the planting plan. Each watering point should be given a value for amount of water to be delivered.

4. The size of tubing for mains and laterals should be based on the amount of water required by each area. Tubing size should allow for some addition of plant material and emission devices without exceeding design limits.

F. INSTALLATION

1. VALVES: See VALVES AND VALVE BOXES.

2. FILTRATION DEVICES: Should be installed per manufacturer's recommendations.

3. TUBING

   a. All tubing should be installed in protected areas to avoid mechanical damage as much as possible.

   b. The tubing should be easy to locate to ensure that it will not be damaged when the planting medium is cultivated. One method that has proven successful is to install the main line around the perimeter of the planting area and run all lateral lines to the individual plants perpendicular to the main line. When buried this way, it is easy to visualize where the lines are located.

   c. Underground installation: Lay out and bury tubing as described in above paragraph.

   d. Surface installation: Where numerous emission devices are used, it may be desirable to run the tubing on the surface. Use sleeves or rigid PVC in areas where damage is likely.

   e. Overhead installation: Tubing may be stapled or clipped to containers or other above ground plantings. Allow six inches per 100 feet of run for expansion and contraction as temperature changes.

4. FITTINGS: All fittings should be installed per manufacturer's recommendations.

5. EMISSION DEVICES

   a. With the exception of soaker tubing, all emission devices should be installed above ground. Some systems work well underground, but if a system becomes contaminated by debris from lack of filtration or from a cut in the line, there is no way to check visually to determine if the system is operable. Above ground installation eliminates this problem.

   b. All emission devices should have stake holders, clips, or other pinning devices to keep them firmly in place.

G. INTERIORSCAPE CONSIDERATIONS

1. No automatic interiorscape system should be installed without adequate drainage. Modern controllers and valves are very reliable, but the failure to plan proper drainage can create tremendous liabilities for the manufacturer, the designer, and the installer.

2. Controller requirements are another concern in automatic watering of interiorscape. With an artificial environment, there is little change in watering, though requirements may go up in winter. If the external irrigation controller also controls the interior, it should be versatile enough for independent cycle timing.

3.12 WINTERIZATION OF IRRIGATION SYSTEMS

A. DESCRIPTION

The purpose of winterization is to adequately protect an irrigation system from winter freezing where installed in a geographic area with continuous cold temperatures likely to cause the freezing of water within the pipes, valves, and other fittings, and subsequently splitting or bursting pipes, valve fittings, and tubing. This can be accomplished by voiding enough water from the system to prevent freeze damage. The methods described below have been proven under cold weather conditions.

B. SLOPE TO DRAIN METHOD

1. All piping should be installed so that it can be drained.

2. Trenching should be graded so as to minimize the number of low points (and subsequent drain valves).

3. After the completion of trenching and the placement of piping in trenches, and prior to backfilling, drain valves and sumps should be installed at predetermined low points in the piping.

4. The type of drain device can be either manually operated on all continuous pressure pipe or of the automatic opening-type option on non-pressure lines.

5. Manual drain valves may be either a globe type or gate type valve and should be located in a valve box. Automatic drain valves should be installed in strict accordance with manufacturer's recommendations and, in addition, should be marked with a valve-marking device. if manual drain valves are used and the valves are located at a depth which does not allow for easy hand operation, the owner should be provided with a valve key of sufficient length to allow for easy operation of the valve.

6. All valves should drain freely either to "daylight" or into a gravel-filled underground sump capable of containing all of the water produced by the section of the system being drained. if a sump is employed, the depth of the sump should be such that when the system is drained the water level in the sump will be at least six inches below the outlet of the valve.

7. If automatic drain valves are used, they should open when the pressure within the system falls below 3 psi.

8. There should be a minimum of one drain valve per operating section. Where slope conditions create excess pressure beyond that for opening an automatic drain, multiple automatic drains or manual drains will be needed. For lines using check valves, manual drains must be properly installed.

C. AIR EVACUATION METHOD

1. This method allows for the introduction of compressed air into the irrigation system to evacuate the water.

2. A gate valve (of full line size of the pipe) should be installed in the irrigation main line at a point where the pipe is still at a frost-free depth, usually immediately after the point of connection to the water source. Immediately downstream of the valve a metallic tee (of full line size) should be installed and 1-inch metallic pipe should be run to ground level. A quick coupling valve should be installed on the pipe at ground level. The shut-off valve should be installed, with a sleeve carried to ground level with either a cap or valve box located at ground level. A permanent valve key with

a tee handle should be attached to the valve-operating handle and should be long enough to allow easy operation from ground level.

3. IT IS OF THE UTMOST IMPORTANCE THAT ALL OF THE PIPING FROM THE QUICK COUPLER TO THE MAIN LINE BE OF GALVANIZED IRON, BRASS, OR COPPER PIPE. A CONSIDERABLE AMOUNT OF HEAT IS GENERATED DURING BLOWOUT OF THE LINES, WHICH WILL MELT PVC OR OTHER PLASTIC PIPE.

4. A quick coupler key (of a size to match the quick coupling valve) should be provided with a hose swivel attached. A standard air compressor hose connector will be attached to the hose swivel.

5. The following procedures should be followed to "blow down" the system:

   a. Prior to the beginning of freezing weather, the main line valve (described above) should be closed completely. An air compressor is connected to the system. The air will be introduced into the system with all valves closed. Once all available space has been filled with air, a sprinkler valve should be opened, allowing the air to enter the system. (Note: Open only one valve at a time!) Allow the air to push water out through the sprinklerheads until a fine mist is achieved. Close the sprinkler valve and allow the pressure to build up in the partially evacuated system for several minutes. Then reopen the sprinkler valve and allow it to remain open until a fine mist is coming from the sprinklers. This step should be repeated until the air flowing from the sprinklers is virtually mist free. (Usually three "blow downs" are required, but more may be required, depending upon the size of the compressor and the overall size of the system.) This procedure should be repeated for each individual section.

   b. It is not possible to specify the compressor size required to properly evacuate all water under different conditions, but a minimum compressor size would be a 65 cfm compressor.

6. A copy of the procedures to "blow down" the system should be given to the Owner or the Owner's representative.

D. PHYSICAL PROTECTION

All exposed equipment adjacent to paved areas that will be snowplowed should be removed and the piping capped and adequately marked.

3.13 AS-BUILT DRAWINGS

A. DESCRIPTION

Irrigation as-built drawings should include the following:

1. Scaled layout of all irrigation components

2. Sizing of all valves, controllers piping, and wire

3. Legend of equipment including symbols, manufacturer's numbers, performance, and description of the equipment

4. Notes of clarification

5. Written irrigation specifications

B. PREPARATION

1. Irrigation as-built drawings are a part of the irrigation installation.

2. Daily entries of the irrigation changes should be recorded.

3. As-built changes should be dimensioned from two permanent points of reference, such as buildings, sidewalks, roadways, lights, or fences.

4. The following items should be recorded prior to backfill:
   a. Irrigation water point of connection
   b. Electrical point of connection
   c. Main line routing
   d. Lateral routing
   e. Electrical wiring routing/splice boxes

5. The location of components of the system should be recorded, including the following:
   a. Controllers
   b. Backflow prevention assembly
   c. Control valves
   d. Gate valves
   e. Drain valves
   f. Pressure reducing valves
   g. Quick coupler valves or hose bibs
   h. Sprinkler heads
   i. Booster pumps
   j. Soil moisture sensors
   k. Filters
   l. Drip emitters

6. Upon completion of the irrigation system, all changes and dimensions should be transferred to a readable irrigation plan.

PART 1 – GENERAL

PART 2 – PRODUCTS

PART 3 – EXECUTION

1.01 DESCRIPTION

Garden lighting provides safety, security, and enhancement of the outdoor environment.

1.02 WORK INCLUDED

This section includes the installation electrical lighting products designed and manufactured specifically for exterior use, including 120 volt and 12 volt cable, wiring, fixtures, and switching.

The provisions of SECTION 1- GENERAL REQUIREMENTS apply to the work under this section as though written herein in full.

1.03 QUALITY ASSURANCE

A. Necessary permits should be secured prior to commencement of work.

B. All 120 volt 'line voltage" wiring and connected equipment should be installed only by a properly licensed contractor and in strict compliance with the requirements of the National Electric Code.

1.04 REFERENCES

NATIONAL ELECTRIC CODE, Current Edition

1.05 SITE CONDITIONS
A. EXISTING CONDITIONS

1. Contractor should be cautious when laying out and trenching for electrical installations. Large roots of trees and shrubs exceeding two inches in diameter should not be cut. If necessary, excavations should be re-routed or tunneled under the roots.

2. Contractor should be responsible for maintaining the existing finish of all walls where switches are installed.

B. ENVIRONMENTAL CONDITIONS

Contractor should be aware of potential "light spillover" or light trespass onto adjacent properties which may violate local ordinances, privacy of neighbors, or cause hazards to vehicular traffic.

1.06 SCHEDULING

A. Contractor should order all light fixtures for the project in ample time to allow for delivery and installation prior to completion of the work.

B. The installation of light fixtures and wiring should be coordinated with the total work schedule, to avoid damage to completed phases of work.

1.07 SUBSTITUTIONS

Substitutions, if necessary due to lack of availability or production delays, should be approved by the Owner or Owner's representative.

1.08 WARRANTY

Contractor should be responsible for quality of materials and workmanship for a period of not less than one year.

2.01 GENERAL

All electrical cables and wire, transformers, controls, and fixtures must meet all requirements of the National Electric Code and should be listed and approved by a nationally recognized electrical testing laboratory.

2.02 GROUND FAULT INTERRUPTERS

All outdoor receptacles and circuits must be protected with an approved ground fault interrupter (GFI) device.

2.03 CONDUIT

All buried conduit should be galvanized rigid metal or SCH 40 polyvinyl chloride PVC pipe, as approved. Thin wall electrical metallic tubing is not allowed.

2.04 12 VOLT CABLE

Cable should be Type UF, stranded, #12 gauge minimum, of "direct burial" quality, covered with insulation treated to inhibit actions of oil, water, salt, and ultraviolet radiation, and to repel rodents.

2.05 12 VOLT TRANSFORMERS

A. Transformers should be manufactured expressly for use in 12 volt lighting systems, sized to supply even power to all lamps on a given portion of a system, and equipped with a three-wire ("U" ground type) six-foot cord and with necessary fittings for rigid electrical conduit connection.

B. "Rain-tight" transformers are required for most exterior installations.

2.06 12 VOLT WIRE SPLICE CONNECTIONS

All electrical splices should be electrically correct with full wire to wire contact. An approved wire splice device should be used. Copper "quick-connect" pin-type coupling devices should not be used.

2.07 CONTROLS AND SWITCHES

A. Time clocks (electro-mechanical or solid state) can be used to control one or more transformers. Time clocks should be of correct load rating, which is determined by the number of outlets to be controlled. All time clocks should be an approved type for the application.

B. Photocells, light-sensitive controls which operate on available light conditions (off during daylight and on at night), can be used to control the lighting system. Photocells should conform to system requirements and be an approved type for the application.

C. Only approved electrical switches should be used for switching.

2.08 JUNCTION BOXES

All junction, splice and connection boxes, and outlets should be of approved type.

2.09 FIXTURES

All fixtures should be rated for exterior installation, durable, and so constructed to withstand the elements for a minimum life use of five years. Fixtures should be supplied complete with luminary holders, ballasts (if any), and necessary tubes or lamps. Fixtures should be as selected by Owner or Owner's representative.

PART 3 — EXECUTION

3.01 GENERAL

A. SUPPLY WIRING

Supply wiring for 120 volt "line voltage" wiring should be placed in rigid metal conduit buried six inches deep or PVC pipe buried 18 inches deep. Type UF direct burial cable should be buried 24 inches deep.

B. RESIDENTIAL EXCEPTION

Residential branch circuits rated 300 volts or less and provided with its own current protection of not more than 30 amps shall be permitted with a cover requirement of 12 inches for PVC conduit or Type UF Direct Burial Cable (National Electrical Code 1987, Article 300-5, Exception No. 4)

C. Junctions, splices, connections, and outlets (120 volt) should be made in approved boxes. Boxes should be placed so the bottom of the box is a minimum of eight inches above finish grade.

3.02 GROUND FAULT INTERRUPTERS

Ground fault interrupters (GFI) must be provided, either built into the individual receptacles or on the circuit breaker, and installed in an approved manner.

3.03 12 VOLT CABLE

A. Cable should be laid loosely to allow freedom of placement of fixtures. Ideal locations for cable burial are in irrigation ditches, under header boards, or at the edge of pavements. Type UF cable should have a minimum cover of six inches.

B. Transformers should be connected to the lighting system with a cable of adequate gauge to carry the maximum amperage generated by the transformer. Minimum size is #12 gauge.

C. Whenever possible on above ground fixtures, connections should be made in the stem of the fixture. All other connections should be made with approved 12 volt wire splice connectors in a protected location that is accessible for future repairs.

3.04 TRANSFORMERS

A. TRANSFORMER SIZE

Transformers should be capable of supplying uniform power to all lamps on a given portion of the system. The size should be determined by the total watts needed. More than one transformer may be necessary. A 250 watt transformer is an industry standard, generating a maximum of 20 amperes at 12 volts and is compatible with #12 gauge direct burial cable.

B. EXTERIOR TRANSFORMERS

Exterior "rain-tight" transformers should be installed in non-flooding locations with at least 12 inches between the bottom of the transformer and the ground.

C. INTERIOR TRANSFORMERS

Interior "non-rain-tight" transformers should be installed in a totally dry interior location, such as a garage, service building, or pool house.

3.05 CONTROLS AND SWITCHING

A. Most control of lighting systems occurs on the 120 volt side of the transformer. Lighting systems often operate on one or more transformers. Switching will operate individual transformers, zones, or entire systems.

B. MANUAL CONTROLS

Ordinary "line voltage" electrical switches should be used to connect 120 volt electrical power sources to transformers.

C. TIME CLOCKS

Should be installed per manufacturer's instructions.

D. PHOTOCELL CONTROLS

Should be installed in areas free of artificial light, shadows from plants, buildings, and other light-dark conditions that might affect the operation of the photocell per manufacturer's instructions.

E. TIME CLOCK/PHOTOCELL COMBINATION

1. A time clock can be used to control power to the master photocell. The photocell, in turn, controls one or more transformers.

2. A time clock can be used to control power to individual photocells that control a single transformer. This allows for varying lighting times and effects.

3.06 FIXTURES

A. All fixtures should be installed per manufacturer's instructions.

B. Fixtures with spike mountings should have metal or rigid non-corrosive spikes which can be set in concrete or driven into firm ground. Ground-mounted should be stabilized with 1/2-inch rebar and stainless-steel clamps.

C. Fixtures designed for tree installation should be secured to the tree with pliable material and checked periodically to prevent damage to the tree.

D. Effective shielding of the lamp should be a most important consideration, as the effects of lighting should be seen, not the light source.

PART 1 – GENERAL

1.01 DESCRIPTION
1.02 WORK INCLUDED
1.03 QUALITY ASSURANCE
1.04 REFERENCES
1.05 SUBMITTALS
1.06 SITE CONDITIONS
1.07 SCHEDULING
1.08 SUBSTITUTIONS
1.09 WARRANTY

PART 2 – PRODUCTS

2.01 GROWING MEDIA
2.02 SOIL AMENDMENTS
2.03 FERTILIZERS
2.04 PLANT MATERIALS
2.05 SOD
2.06 SEED
2.07 OTHER MATERIALS

PART 3 – EXECUTION

3.01 SOIL PREPARATION
3.02 PLANTING HOLES
3.03 TREE AND SHRUB PLANTING PROCEDURES
3.04 GROUND COVER PLANTING PROCEDURES
3.05 FINAL GRADING
3.06 TREE STAKING AND GUYING
3.07 CHEMICAL WEED CONTROL
3.08 MULCHING
3.09 SODDED LAWN PLANTING PROCEDURES
3.10 SEEDED LAWN PLANTING PROCEDURES
3.11 PLANT ESTABLISHMENT MAINTENANCE

1.01 DESCRIPTION

Planting is the installation of trees, shrubs, vines, ground covers, lawn, perennials and annuals, and other related materials to provide functional and esthetic enhancement of the outdoor environment and otherwise complete the landscape.

1.02 WORK INCLUDED

This section includes soil preparation, installation of plant materials, pre-emergent weed control, mulching, and other related work.

The provisions of SECTION 1- GENERAL REQUIREMENTS apply to the work under this section as though written herein in full.

1.03 QUALITY ASSURANCE

Soil analysis may be required to determine the proper soil amendments and fertilizers required for the site.

1.04 REFERENCES

CALIFORNIA FOOD AND AGRICULTURE CODE
SUNSET WESTERN GARDEN BOOK
UNIVERSITY OF CALIFORNIA agricultural publications

1.05 SUBMITTALS

Samples of materials may be required.

1.06 SITE CONDITIONS

A. EXISTING CONDITIONS

Rough grading, underground utilities, and site improvements should be completed prior to commencement of planting.

B. ENVIRONMENTAL CONDITIONS

Soil should not be worked in a wet or muddy condition.

1.07 SCHEDULING

Planting operations should be scheduled to avoid unnecessary holding of perishable plant materials and as required to satisfy the job requirements.

1.08 SUBSTITUTIONS

Plant material substitutions should be of similar growth habit and requirements, size, texture, and color. Substitutions must be approved by the Owner or the Owner's representative.

1.09 WARRANTY

Contractor should be responsible for the quality of all materials and workmanship of a minimum period of 90 days following completion of installation and final inspection and acceptance.

2.01 GROWING MEDIA

A. Growing media should be fertile and friable and of such quality that will promote the healthy growth of the plant material.

B. Soil should be reasonably free of rocks, debris, and all noxious weeds.

C. Imported soil, if required, should be free of diseases, pests, and all noxious weeds, and should be of similar texture to the native material on the site, provided the existing native material is suitable. All imported soil should be blended to a depth of three to six inches with the sub-grade material, to prevent interface.

2.02 SOIL AMENDMENTS

Soil amendments should be a wood or bark product, or other relatively dry organic matter. They should not contain noxious vegetation pathogenic viruses, herbicides, or chemicals that could inhibit plant growth. All amendments should comply with the California Food and Agriculture Code.

2.03 FERTILIZERS

Commercial fertilizers may be in pellet, tablet, granular, or liquid formulas and should comply with the chemical analysis specified. All fertilizers must conform to the requirements of the California Food and Agriculture Code.

2.04 PLANT MATERIALS

A. Quality and size of plant materials should conform to the California Grading Code of Nursery Stock, No. 1 grade. This requires that stock, when sold, should not be dead or in a dying condition, frozen, or damaged, and should not show evidence of having had root restriction in previous containers or be abnormally pot-bound. All plants should be of a reasonably uniform and standard size for each species, well formed, and in a healthy, fully rooted, thriving condition.

B. All plants should be true to type or name, by species and variety, as required by the California Food and Agriculture Code.

C. All plants should be typical of their species and variety and should have normal habit of growth. The top growth should be structured proportionately so that it is representative of the species.

D. All plants should comply with Federal and State laws requiring inspection for plant diseases and infestations. Inspection certificates required by law should accompany each shipment of plants, unless plants are authorized to be collected.

E. Container-grown plants should be sufficiently established so that a minimum of 75% of each root ball stays intact during planting. When lifted by the trunk, the trunk should rise no more than one inch before the soil surface of the root ball begins to rise. When unsupported, the trunk of trees should lean no more than 30 degrees from the vertical when measured within four inches of the root ball.

F. Ground cover plants: All rooted cuttings should be healthy, vegetative material with well-established roots at one or more nodes. All container-grown ground cover should be well rooted within the rooting medium.

2.05 SOD

All sod should be freshly cut sod grown from high-quality, propagative material and relatively free of weeds, diseases, and insects. Sod should be machine-cut at a uniform thickness, width, and length and should be well enough developed to resist tearing during handling operations. Sod should not be held or stored for a period of time that allows for decomposition of the grass and roots.

2.06 SEED

All seed should be labeled in accordance with the California Food and Agriculture Code.

2.07 OTHER MATERIALS

A. TREE STAKES

Stakes should be of sufficient size, height, and strength to support the tree in an upright position for a sufficient period of time, to allow for proper trunk growth.

B. TREE TIES

Ties should be of durable, non-abrasive material, with adequate fasteners to secure the tree to the stake. Tree ties should be of such quality to remain intact as long as needed by the plant.

C. CHEMICAL WEED CONTROLS

All chemical weed controls (herbicides) MUST be registered in the State of California and conform to all requirements of the California Food and Agriculture Code. Types include contact, translocated, pre-plant, and pre-emergent herbicides.

D. MULCH

Suitable mulch materials include ground bark, wood chips, compost, and gravel.

PART 3 — EXECUTION

3.01 SOIL PREPARATION

A. Preparation of planting areas should consist of cultivation, incorporation of soil amendments and fertilizers as needed, and finish grading.

B. Planting areas should be cultivated to a minimum depth of six inches to completely break up any compacted soil.

C. Additives should be uniformly placed and incorporated into the soil as required, or in accordance with the recommendations of a qualified soil laboratory and/or proven, local needs.

D. After all amendments have been incorporated, planted areas should be finish graded to re-establish all swales and grades to ensure proper surface drainage. Final grade should be set at a level below sidewalks, curbs, and similar surfaces which will allow for surface drainage after placement of sod, seed, or mulch. All areas should be sloped to drain at the following percentages:

> Adjacent to Buildings .... 2 -10%
> Lawn and Turf Areas .... 1$^{1/2}$ -10%
> Slopes with Plants .... 3 - 20%
> Athletic Fields .... 1 - 2%

E. All planting areas should be smooth, and free of rocks and clay lumps in excess of one inch.

3.02 PLANTING HOLES

A. Plant hole preparation consists of laying out plant locations, digging holes, and placing required additives, if needed.

B. Plant locations should be laid out as indicated on the drawings, adjusting as necessary to avoid existing underground and overhead utilities. Plants should be located where they will not obstruct irrigation sprinklers or drainage swales and far enough away from thoroughfares so they will not encroach when they reach their ultimate size.

C. Plant holes should be excavated to a minimum of two times the diameter of the root ball and 1-1/2 times the depth of the root ball. The sides of holes should be scarified if glazing occurs during excavation. Deeper holes may be required to overcome site conditions, such as compacted, engineered fill or natural stratification, and to improve drainage in the root zone.

D. Additives should be placed in each plant hole, if required. This may be accomplished by placing additives in the plant hole and mixing with native material or by removing all material from the plant hole, mixing additives, and backfilling to a depth that will allow placement of the plant.

E. To avoid uncontrolled future settling of loose material in the plant hole, water should be applied to the lower portion of the backfill with a pipe or tube inserted to the bottom of the excavation, if necessary, until the backfill is saturated for the full depth.

3.03 TREE AND SHRUB PLANTING PROCEDURES

A. Plants should be removed from the containers in a manner to minimize disturbance of the plant and root ball. Circling roots at the periphery of the root ball should be pulled outward or pruned during planting to prevent future girdling.

B. Each plant should be placed in the hole at such a depth that, after the soil has settled, the top of the root ball will be slightly above the surrounding soil, to avoid water accumulation at the crown of the plant. Backfill should be placed around the root ball, using the backfill material from the plant hole preparation.

C. The backfill material and root ball should be saturated to the full depth immediately after planting.

D. Basins should be constructed to allow retention of two inches minimum of water over the top of the root ball. Slope plantings may not require up-slope berms, but will require higher down-slope berms.

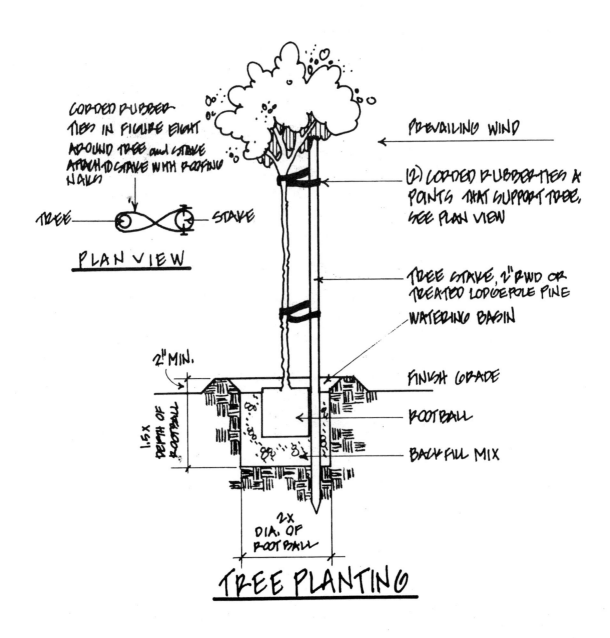

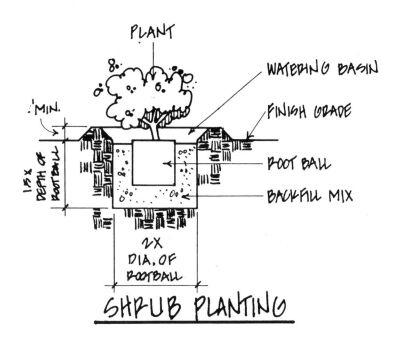

PLANT

WATERING BASIN

FINISH GRADE

ROOT BALL

BACKFILL MIX

MIN.

1.5 X DEPTH OF ROOTBALL

2X DIA. OF ROOTBALL

SHRUB PLANTING

3.04 GROUND COVER PLANTING PROCEDURES

Prior to planting ground cover plants, soil amendments and fertilizers, if used, should be uniformly incorporated into the soil and finish grade established. Plants should be evenly spaced at the required spacing, planted in moist soil, and watered thoroughly immediately after planting.

3.05 FINAL GRADING

Upon completion of planting of trees, shrubs, and ground covers, and prior to the application of pre-emergent weed control and mulch, all planting areas should be final graded to re-establish proper grades, and raked smooth and clean. All debris, and rock or clay lumps one inch and larger should be removed.

3.06 TREE STAKING AND GUYING

Trees should be staked or guyed, as necessary, to keep them in an upright position and hold them erect, while allowing the tops and trunks to flex with the wind. Short, stocky trees may require a minimum of support at the base. When single staking, stakes should be placed on the upwind side of the trees. Tree trunks and lateral branches should be protected from unnecessary abrasion from stakes and ties. Tree stakes should not be bound up against the tree trunks and should not shade the tree trunks unnecessarily.

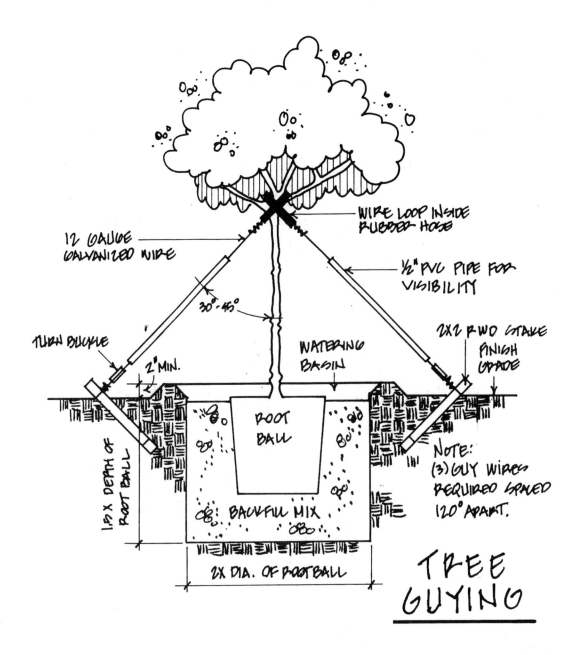

TREE GUYING

Labels on diagram:
- 12 GAUGE GALVANIZED WIRE
- WIRE LOOP INSIDE RUBBER HOSE
- ½" PVC PIPE FOR VISIBILITY
- 30°-45°
- TURN BUCKLE
- 2" MIN.
- WATERING BASIN
- 2X2 RWD STAKE FINISH GRADE
- 1.5X DEPTH OF ROOT BALL
- ROOT BALL
- BACKFILL MIX
- NOTE: (3) GUY WIRES REQUIRED SPACED 120° APART.
- 2X DIA. OF ROOTBALL

3.07 CHEMICAL WEED CONTROL

Herbicides used for chemical weed control should be applied per the manufacturer's recommendations and must be done in accordance with all regulations of government agencies. Use extreme care when using herbicides to avoid the risk of damage to other plant materials or injury to humans and wildlife.

3.08 MULCHING

Planting areas should be mulched to help keep the soil and young plant roots at a desirable temperature, maintain moisture, and reduce weed growth. Mulch should be applied in an even and smooth layer over the planting area after final grading is complete and after the application of an appropriate herbicide, if used.

126

3.09 SODDED LAWN PLANTING PROCEDURES

A. After soil preparation is complete, the finish grade of areas to be sodded should be approximately one inch below the surface of adjacent paving or other edging.

B. A suitable fertilizer should be applied, following manufacturer's recommendation, and the soil moistened, prior to sodding.

C. Sod should be laid with staggered, butted joints and should be in firm contact with the soil, with no spaces between the joints.

D. Sod should be rolled immediately following installation and prior to initial watering; heavy water saturation of the sod, in lieu of rolling, is acceptable if a tight bond can be ensured.

E. Proper moisture should be provided throughout the sod to avoid unnecessary stress to the plant material. Sod should be thoroughly watered upon completion of installation and proper soil moisture level maintained thereafter.

F. The first mowing should be done before the grass reaches four inches in height and when the soil is in a relatively firm condition. No more than one-third of the leaf surface should be removed with any single mowing.

3.10 SEEDED LAWN PLANTING PROCEDURES

A. After planting area has been prepared, seeds and fertilizers, per manufacturer's recommendations or as specified, should be evenly distributed and incorporated by raking, cultipacking, or other accepted methods, and the area top-dressed with mulch when necessary.

B. No incorporation of seed, and top-dress fertilizer is necessary when seeding hydraulically with an adequate amount of mulch.

C. The watering program does not have to begin immediately after completion of seeding operations, as long as the soil is not moist enough to initiate germination. During the germination period, the surface should be kept moist at all times, avoiding all water runoff.

D. Seeded lawns should be mowed before the grass reaches four inches in height and when the soil is in a relatively firm condition. No more than one-third of the leaf surface should be removed at any single mowing.

3.11 PLANT ESTABLISHMENT MAINTENANCE
REFER TO SECTION VII - MAINTENANCE

PART 1 – GENERAL

1.01	DESCRIPTION
1.02	WORK INCLUDED
1.03	QUALITY ASSURANCE
1.04	REFERENCES
1.05	SITE CONDITIONS
1.06	SCHEDULING
1.07	WARRANTY
1.08	EQUIPMENT

PART 2 – PRODUCTS

2.01	FERTILIZERS
2.02	PESTICIDES
2.03	HERBICIDES (CHEMICAL WEED CONTROL)
2.04	GROWTH REGULATORS

PART 3 – EXECUTION

3.01	TREES
3.02	SHRUBS AND VINES
3.03	GROUND COVERS
3.04	LAWNS
3.05	IRRIGATION SYSTEMS
3.06	DRAINAGE SYSTEMS
3.07	DISEASE AND PEST CONTROL
3.08	WEED CONTROL
3.09	GROWTH REGULATORS
3.10	DEBRIS REMOVAL

1.01 DESCRIPTION

Landscape maintenance preserves and sustains the quality of a landscape. Landscapes are generally designed with a given style, formal or informal; proper maintenance maintains the intended design concept.

1.02 WORK INCLUDED

This section includes the maintenance of plantings, irrigation and drainage systems, debris removal, and other related work.

The provisions of SECTION 1 - GENERAL REQUIREMENTS apply to the work under this section as though written herein in full.

1.03 QUALITY ASSURANCE

Contractor must be properly licensed and registered to perform pest control work included in this section.

1.04 REFERENCES

CALIFORNIA FOOD AND AGRICULTURE CODE
SUNSET WESTERN GARDEN BOOK
UNIVERSITY OF CALIFORNIA agricultural publications

1.05 SITE CONDITIONS

A. EXISTING CONDITIONS

1. Contractor should inspect the entire site and be familiar with the requirements and growth habits of all existing plant material.

2. Prior to commencement of work, the Contractor should advise the Owner or Owner's representative of existing conditions which may affect the project.

B. ENVIRONMENTAL CONDITIONS

Contractor should advise the Owner or Owner's representative of serious disease or pest problems and any other conditions which may be detrimental to the condition of the landscape.

1.06 SCHEDULING

Maintenance services should be provided on a weekly basis, Monday through Saturday, between the hours of 7 a.m. and 6 p.m., unless other arrangements have been made with the Owner or Owner's representative.

1.07 WARRANTY

A. Contractor should furnish all supervision, labor, materials, and equipment necessary for the complete maintenance of all landscaped areas.

B. Plant materials should be maintained in a healthy and vigorous condition, irrigation and drainage systems kept in good working order, and the general site kept clean.

C. Contractor should restore or replace any trees, shrubs, ground covers, lawn, perennials, or annuals damaged by Contractor's action or lack of action.

D. Contractor should not be responsible for the following, unless specifically agreed upon with the Owner or Owner's representative:

1. Pruning and pest control of trees exceeding 15 feet in height
2. Repair or replacement of irrigation main lines, controllers, valves, and worn components
3. Replacement of plant material damaged or destroyed by irrigation system failure, storms, or other causes beyond the Contractor's control
4. Renovation of ground covers
5. Thatching of turf grass areas
6. Rotation of annual color
7. Damage caused by rodents or other pests

1.08 EQUIPMENT

Contractor should provide and maintain all equipment necessary to properly complete the maintenance work. Equipment should be safe, proper, efficient, and suited to and for the job. All cutting blades should be kept properly sharpened. All equipment must have all required safety devices in place and in operation.

PART 2 — PRODUCTS

2.01 FERTILIZERS

Commercial fertilizers may be pellet, tablet, granular, or liquid form and must conform to the requirements of the California Food and Agriculture Code. Choice of fertilizers should be based on soil fertility tests and/or the specific plant requirements.

2.02 PESTICIDES

All pesticides MUST be registered in the State of California and conform to all requirements of the California Food and Agriculture Code.

2.03 HERBICIDES

All herbicides MUST be registered in the State of California and conform to all requirements of the California Food and Agriculture Code.

2.04 GROWTH REGULATORS

Growth regulators must be registered in the State of California and conform to all requirements of the California Food and Agriculture Code.

3.01 TREES
A. PRUNING

1. All trees should be allowed to grow to their natural genetic form and size, unless specifically excepted.

2. Tree pruning should have two basic objectives: to promote structural strength and to accentuate the natural form and features of the tree.

3. The primary pruning of deciduous trees should be done during the dormant season. Damaged trees or those that constitute health or safety hazards should be pruned at any time of the year, as required.

4. Under no circumstances should stripping of lower branches ("raising up") of young trees be permitted. Lower branches should be retained in a "tipped back" or pinched condition with as much foliage as possible to promote calipered trunk growth ("tapered trunk"). Lower branches should be cut off only after the tree is able to stand erect without staking or other support.

5. Trees with a strong central leader and conical (pyramidal) shape generally need little or no pruning. As a rule, the single central leader should never be radically topped or cut back, as this will create an unnatural multi-leader form and an abundance of weak vegetative growth.

6. Trees with multi-leaders or a branched main trunk system should be pruned to select and develop permanent scaffold branches which have vertical spacing from 18 to 24 inches and radial orientation so as not to overlay one another. This is done to eliminate narrow, V-shaped branch forks that lack strength, to maintain growth within space limitations, and to maintain a natural appearance.

7. Conifers should be thinned out and shaped only when necessary, to prevent wind and storm damage.

8. Proper side branch removal requires cutting at the main trunk just beyond the branch bark ridges.

9. All suckers and water sprouts and crisscrossing dead, diseased, broken, and heavily ladened side branches should be removed to thin crown for less wind resistance.

B. IRRIGATION

1. Trees have deep root systems. Soil conditions should be monitored closely for both under- and over-watering.

2. Frequency and duration of irrigation should be dictated by the requirements of the specific trees.

3. All trees should be probed with a soil sampling probe to a depth of 24 inches at least every 45 days to ascertain the subsoil conditions. A saturated condition is an indication of drainage problems or excessive irrigation and should be corrected as soon as possible.

C. FERTILIZATION

1. Most trees should be fertilized annually, in the spring, with a complete fertilizer.

2. Fertilization of mature trees should be required only if the trees show a definite need for fertilization.

3. Apply fertilizer around the tree, approximately halfway between the base and dripline, at a rate of one-half pound of actual nitrogen per inch of trunk diameter measured at four feet above the soil surface.

D. STAKING AND GUYING

1. The purpose of staking and guying trees is to support and protect young trees until such time as they can stand alone.

2. All tree stakes, guys, and ties should be maintained to properly support the tree and should be inspected every 90 days, to prevent girdling or chafing of trunks or branches or rubbing that may cause bark wounds.

3. Stakes and guys should be removed when no longer required for support.

E. TREE WELLS

1. Bare soil wells should be maintained around all trees. A circle with a radius of 12 inches beyond the bark of the tree should be maintained free of grass, ground covers, and weeds.

2. Grasses and weeds should be removed or sprayed with a contact herbicide *(see Weed Control)*.

3.02 SHRUBS AND VINES
A. PRUNING

1. The general objectives for pruning of shrubs and vines are to maintain growth within space limitations, to maintain a natural appearance, to eliminate diseased or damaged growth, and to select and develop permanent branches.

2. General pruning should be done in late winter. Minor pruning may be done at any time.

3. Shrubs should be pruned to conform with the design concept of the landscape.

4. Individual shrubs should not be clipped into balled or boxed forms, except in formal gardens.

5. Vines should be pruned to control growth and direction, and should be kept "in-bounds" and not allowed to grow over windows, doors, gates, or other structural features.

6. All pruning cuts should be made to lateral branches or buds or flush with trunk or main stem. Pinching or light heading back of terminal buds on selected shrub species promotes bushiness. To prevent legginess (sparse lower branches), shrubs should be maintained with the lower foliage wider than the upper foliage. This practice allows more light to reach the lower foliage.

B. IRRIGATION

1. Frequency and duration of irrigation should be dictated by the specific requirement of the shrubs and vines.

2. Soil moisture checks of representative plants in the landscape should be made bimonthly, using a soil sampling probe or other approved tool.

3. Consideration should be given to the ground covers growing in shrub areas. Irrigation scheduling should be based on the requirements of the shallowest rooted plants in the area.

C. FERTILIZATION

1. Most shrubs and vines should be fertilized annually. Plants that have reached maturity may not require annual fertilization. Plants requiring continual or annual pruning, due to space limitations or espaliering, may require more frequent fertilization.

2. All actively growing plants not yet at maturity should be fertilized once per year in the spring (March or April). Apply an appropriate slow-release, long lasting nitrogen fertilizer, controlled-release fertilizer, or plant tablets at the manufacturer's recommended application rate.

3.03 GROUND COVERS
A. EDGING

1. Established ground covers bordering sidewalks or curbs should be edged as often as necessary to provide a clean, crisp line at all times.

2. Ground covers should not be allowed to touch or cover the crowns of shrubs and trees.

B. IRRIGATION

1. Ground covers should be irrigated according to the water requirements of the plants. Because both trees and shrubs are often planted in ground cover areas, irrigation should be made with the water requirements of all plants considered.

2. Moisture checks should be made periodically by use of a soil probe in various ground cover areas. These checks should be used as a guide in water requirements.

C. FERTILIZATION

1. Fertilization should coincide with the ground cover growing season. One application of a complete fertilizer applied in the spring, per manufacturer's recommended application rate, is generally adequate for established ground covers.

2. Young or sparse ground cover areas require a minimum of two applications of fertilizer: one in early spring and again in late spring or early summer.

D. RENOVATION

1. Ground covers will develop a thatch layer with age. This mat of old stems (thatch) is not only unsightly, but harbors a great number of insects, rodents, and other undesirable pests.

2. Renovation of ground covers is normally done at the end of the dormant season, and will reduce the thatch and revitalize the appearance of the ground cover.

E. COVERAGE

In order to establish complete coverage within a maximum of two growing seasons, ground cover plantings should be kept healthy and actively growing with proper irrigation and fertilization.

3.04 LAWNS
A. MOWING

1. Lawns should be mowed weekly during the growing season and at other times as needed.

2. Because of their physiology, cool season grasses should be mowed at a medium high cut. Seasonally, the lawns should be cut at no less than the following heights:

    March through May .... 1-1/2 inches
    June through August .... 2 inches
    September through November .... 1-1$^{1/2}$ inches
    December through February .... 1 inch

3. As a general rule, warm season grasses are mowed shorter than cool season grasses. Begin mowing at one-half inch in the spring and slowly adjust to one inch by late summer and early fall. Avoid scalping during the growing season.

4. Mowing patterns should be alternated each week, to avoid creating ruts and compaction.

5. Clippings should either be caught or vacuumed from the lawns.

6. Annual thatch removal (vertical mowing) should be done during the early spring months.

B. EDGING

1. All lawn edges along sidewalks and curbs, as well as shrub or ground cover border areas, should be edged at least every two weeks during the active growing season, March through October, and as required for appearance for the remainder of the year.

2. Edging should be performed with a blade type mechanical edger. The cut edge should appear as a clean, smooth line.

3. Obstacles within the lawn areas should be edged to maintain a grass-free clear space of two inches in width.

4. Lawn sprinkler heads should only be edged to allow for proper distribution of water.

C. AERATION

1. Lawns should be plugged or aerated at least twice per year, once in the spring and again in the fall.

2. Spring and fall fertilization should take place at this time.

D. IRRIGATION

1. Lawns should be irrigated at such frequency as weather conditions require. Soil moisture within the root zones should remain constant and adequate during the growing season.

2. Lawns should not be watered on the day prior to mowing and daily watering should be discouraged. Wet soil conditions usually promote disease and soil compaction.

3. Lawns should be irrigated at night or early morning. Wherever possible, intermittent applications during the irrigation period should be used to increase penetration and eliminate runoff.

E. FERTILIZATION

1. Depending on type of grass, normal requirements of actual nitrogen are five to nine pounds per 1,000 square feet per year.

2. Availability of nitrogen should be as even as possible. Not more than one pound per month should be applied during the growing season.

3. Fertilizers should be applied per the manufacturer's recommendations.

3.05 IRRIGATION SYSTEMS
A. GENERAL

1. Proper irrigation system maintenance includes the overall supervision of the system, controller scheduling, routine adjustments, and necessary repairs.

2. Failure of the system to provide full and proper coverage should not relieve the Contractor of providing adequate coverage.

B. CONTROLLER SCHEDULING

1. A qualified person should be completely responsible for operating the irrigation systems, with the duties of adjusting controllers, observing the effectiveness of the irrigation system, and making minor adjustments to the system.

2. The irrigation programs should be adjusted to conform to plant requirements, soil and slope conditions, weather, and change of seasons, within the limitations of the system.

3. Water should not be applied at a rate higher than the infiltration rate of the soil.

4. A soil sampling probe and/or a tensiometer should be used regularly to evaluate actual soil moisture levels and irrigation schedule.

5. Automatic irrigation controllers should be rescheduled, as necessary, to avoid water waste and runoff, and should be turned off during periods of rain.

6. In windy areas the controllers should be set to operate during periods of low wind velocity.

7. Watering schedules should be arranged so as not to interfere with the use of the facility.

8. A chart should be maintained to record current irrigation programs, including day, time, and length of watering for each station and program for each controller.

C. SYSTEM MAINTENANCE

1. The irrigation system should be maintained for optimum performance. This should include cleaning and adjusting all sprinkler heads and valves for proper coverage.

2. Inspections of the irrigation system, in operation, should be made weekly during summer months, April through October, and biweekly November through March, to detect any malfunctioning of the system.

3. All malfunctioning equipment should be repaired prior to the next scheduled irrigation.

4. All replacement heads should be of the same manufacturer, type, and application rates.

3.06 DRAINAGE SYSTEMS

A. Good drainage is essential for healthy and vigorous plant growth, and systems must be routinely checked for blockage which could cause ponding, flooding, and excessive saturation of the soil and plant root zones.

B. Surface drainage swales should be kept free of leaves, debris, and sediment accumulations.

C. Underground drainage systems should be flushed with water at least twice a year, summer and winter, to avoid plugged pipes.

3.07 DISEASE AND PEST CONTROL

A. All chemical controls MUST be applied under the strict supervision of a licensed and qualified pest control applicator, per the manufacturer's recommended label application procedures.

B. Healthy plants and lawns should be able to withstand minor disease and insect damage without controls. Routine applications of pesticides should not be permitted, as this practice destroys natural predator-prey relationships in the environment.

C. In general, with proper fertilization and irrigation practices the incidence of serious disease and insect problems can be reduced.

D. Where unusually high infections or infestations occur, an accurate identification of the disease or insect should be made and the control product selected with care, prior to application.

E. Insecticidal soaps should be utilized, whenever possible.

F. Snails and slugs should be controlled with recommended baits and sprays.

G. Rodents such as gophers and moles should be trapped or controlled with approved baits.

3.08 WEED CONTROL
A. USE OF HERBICIDES

Herbicides may be used to control and inhibit weed growth, but must be selected with extreme care. Pre-plant, pre-emergent, contact, and translocated herbicides are available. Some herbicides can cause damage to plant material. Herbicides must be applied in strict accordance with manufacturer's label application procedures.

B. TREE WELLS

Contact herbicides may be used to control the growth of weeds and grasses in tree wells but should not be used more than once a month. Avoid spray contact with the tree bark. Pre-emergent herbicides may be used. Caution must be exercised to avoid damage to adjacent lawns or ground covers.

C. SHRUB AND GROUND COVER AREAS

Shrub and ground cover areas should be maintained free of weeds and grasses. Herbicides may be used to control weed growth. Careful consideration should be given to the choice of materials used. Some herbicides will damage turf grass and some ground covers. Use caution in application in areas adjacent to lawns or ground covers.

D. LAWNS

1. Weeds should not be a major problem in a properly maintained lawn. Weed infestations are usually caused or encouraged by improper mowing, watering, or fertilization.

2. If weeds have resulted from poor maintenance, the deficient practice should be corrected.

3. Before selecting and applying herbicides to lawns, the type of weed should be carefully identified.

4. Herbicides should be used as little as possible. Only when necessary should herbicides be used as a means of swinging the weed-grass competition in favor of the turf grass.

E. OTHER WEED CONTROL

Weeds should not be allowed to grow in paved areas such as driveways, curbs, walks, and paths. Weeds can be removed manually or herbicides may be used for control. The use of weed oil, diesel fuel, or other staining or damaging materials shall not be allowed. Dead weeds should be removed from all pavements.

3.09 GROWTH REGULATORS

Growth regulators may be used to control the growth of some plant material with careful selection, but should be used only as directed by the manufacturer's recommended application procedures.

3.10 DEBRIS REMOVAL

A. Litter and trash including leaves, rubbish, papers, bottles, cans, and other debris should be removed from all areas of the site on a weekly basis.

B. All refuse from the maintenance operation should be disposed of off the property.

PART 1 – GENERAL

PART 2 – PRODUCTS

PART 3 – EXECUTION

1.01 DESCRIPTION

Interiorscaping is the use of living plants and related products in public, commercial, and private interior spaces to provide a functional and aesthetic enhancement of the interior environment.

1.02 WORK INCLUDED

This section includes the installation of plant materials, decorative containers, drainage and irrigation systems, and the maintenance of such improvements.

The provisions of SECTION I - GENERAL REQUIREMENTS apply to the work under this section as though written herein in full.

1.03 QUALITY ASSURANCE

Contractor must be properly licensed and registered to perform pest control work.

1.04 REFERENCES

CALIFORNIA FOOD AND AGRICULTURE CODE

1.05 SUBMITTALS

Owner may require Contractor to submit samples of decorative containers and plant material. If required, the Contractor should arrange for the Owner or Owner's representative to inspect and approve all plant material prior to commencement of work.

1.06 ENVIRONMENTAL REQUIREMENTS

Owner should be responsible for ensuring that the best possible environmental conditions are maintained.

A. Air circulation, whether natural or by air conditioner, must be as consistent as possible.

B. Pollution of the air supply with dust, gases, or toxic elements should not be allowed.

C. Owner should be aware that vapors from mercury-based paints, which may be present in the environment, are extremely detrimental to certain plants.

D. Appropriate light intensity and duration (foot-candle hours) must be provided and maintained to supply the requirements of the plants.

1.07 SCHEDULING

Contractor should make every possible effort to schedule the work in a manner that will least interrupt the functioning of the facility.

1.08 SUBSTITUTIONS

Substitutions of plant materials should be made with plants of similar species and variety. Substitutions of decorative containers should be made only with the approval of the Owner or Owner's representative.

1.09   WARRANTY

A.   Contractor should be responsible for the quality of all materials and workmanship for a minimum period of 90 days following completion of installation, final inspection, and acceptance.

1. At any time within this period the Contractor should replace any plant that is not in a healthy, attractive condition.

2. Plant replacements should be made only with the same species, variety, and size or, with the approval of the Owner or Owner's representative, with a plant of similar character, size, and value.

B.   Contractor should not be responsible for the replacement or repair of plants damaged by the following.

1. Extreme changes in temperature, changes in the normal temperatures maintained at the site, prolonged absence of proper lighting conditions, or the pollution of the air quality.

2. Vandalism or extreme conditions beyond the Contractor's control.

3. Accidental or malicious treatment by site employees, janitorial or other personnel, or by visitors to the site including the pouring of liquids, such as coffee or soft drinks, into plant containers.

4. Relocations or positioning of plants by others.

5. Watering or other well-meaning care by Owner, Owner's employees, or visitors.

PART 2 - PRODUCTS

2.01   PLANT MATERIALS

A.   All plants should be true to type or name and typical of the species or variety.

B.   All plants should be in a healthy, thriving condition, and must be free of all diseases and pests.

C.   All plants should be nursery-grown unless specifically authorized to be collected.

D.   All plants should have normal habit of growth, and the top should be structured proportionately.

E.   Height and width of individual plants of a species or variety should not vary more than 10 percent, and the caliper of the stems should be sufficient to support the top growth without considerable separate support.

F.   Root development of all plant material should be healthy, vigorous growth, typical of the particular species in the specified environment. Upon inspection, root growth should be visible throughout the entire container root medium area.

2.02   PLANTING MEDIA

A.   The planting medium should be uniform and comprised of such components and proportions as may be necessary to provide the following.

1. Thorough drainage and satisfactory aeration of root zone.

2. Adequate moisture and nutrient retention as is necessary to sustain controlled plant growth.

B. The planting medium should be free of pests, pathogens, weeds, fertilizer buildup, chemical residues, or any other contaminates.

2.03 CONTAINERS

A. BUILT-IN PLANTERS
This type of planter is generally in place at the site.

B. DECORATIVE CONTAINERS

1. Free-standing decorative containers should be of a quality suitable to interiors.

2. The material and construction of the container should be durable and appropriate for the site situation (traffic patterns, methods of cleaning, etc.).

3. Ceramic, terra cotta and plastic pots, baskets, controlled watering containers, and other specified containers may be used.

2.04 CONTAINER LINING MATERIAL
Plastic sheeting, 8-10 mil.

2.05 DRAINAGE MATERIALS

A. DRAINAGE FILL
Bark or clean gravel.

B. SOIL SEPARATOR
Filter Fabric: Manufacturer's standard non-woven geotextile fabric of polypropylene, polyester fibers, or combination of the two, or other suitable material.

C. SIPHON TUBES
Rigid plastic polyvinyl chloride (PVC) pipe and caps. 1-1/2 inch diameter pipe is generally used.

2.06 IRRIGATION MATERIALS
REFER TO IRRIGATION - PART 2

2.07 OTHER MATERIALS

A. CONTAINER FILL MATERIAL
Bark, perlite, Styrofoam, drain rock, or gravel are acceptable.

B. TOP DRESSING MATERIALS
Suitable materials include sphagnum moss, Spanish moss, bark chips, cypress shavings, and decorative rock or gravel.

2.08 FERTILIZERS
Commercial fertilizers may be pellet, tablet, granular, or liquid form and must conform to the requirements of the California Food and Agriculture Code.

2.09 PESTICIDES

All pesticides MUST be registered in the State of California for INDOOR USE and conform to all requirements of the California Food and Agriculture Code.

3.01 DESIGN CONSIDERATIONS

A. PLANT SELECTION

1. Should be horticulturally correct for the given interior site environment, aesthetically pleasing, and in keeping with the interior decor.

2. Careful consideration should be given to the following.

   a. Light tolerance of plant species in relation to the available light intensity and light duration at the site.

   b. The scale of the plant in relation to the interior space.

   c. The color and texture of the plant foliage.

3. Hanging plants should be used with caution. The weight of the container and the strength of the ceiling fixture should be carefully evaluated. Written permission should be obtained from the Owner or Owner's representative prior to installing hanging plants.

B. DECORATIVE CONTAINERS

1. Free-standing containers should be of a character and quality in keeping with the interior decor.

2. The shape and size of the container should be selected in relation to the size of the plant's nursery pot, the size of the plant itself, and the scale of the interior.

3. Color and texture of the container should relate to the color scheme of the interior decor and the plant material to be used.

C. DRAINAGE

Adequate drainage is required to drain excess water away from plant root systems. One of the following acceptable methods should be used.

1. Drainage holes in container with saucer.

2. Double potting with drainage catch basin.

3. Drainage catch basin with a water siphoning system.

4. Drainage integral to an underground drainage system. Generally installed in built-in planters.

D. IRRIGATION

1. Adequate watering systems are necessary to maintain specific plant needs, with special consideration given to interior use.

2. There should be limited or controlled use of overhead spray irrigation systems.

3. The use of drip irrigation and mini-spray systems or controlled watering containers is desirable.

E. TOP DRESSING
Should be required to create a finished and professional finished appearance.

3.02 PLANT ACCLIMATION

A. All plants should be acclimated, as required by the species, to the specific conditions of the site location.

B. If plants have not been acclimated for the specific conditions of the site by the grower, acclimation should be affected by one or more or all of the following procedures.

1. Exposure to reduced light intensity, to match the future environment, for 30 days or more.

2. Change in root system medium type, only when necessary.

3. Introduction of an appropriate fertilization program. In most cases, this should be less frequent and reduced quantities of any needed supplemental fertilizers than used in most growing situations.

4. Reduction of total soluble salt content, where necessary. This may require leeching of root zone to achieve soluble salt levels of no more than 700 ppm.

5. Stabilization of pH level to 6.0-6.5.

6. Less frequent watering. Acclimation practices reduce water requirements. Water only as necessary.

3.03 INSTALLATION PROCEDURES
A. DOUBLE POTTING
Placement of plant in its nursery-grown pot directly into a decorative freestanding container or built-in planter.

1. Container or planter should be lined with plastic sheeting to prevent moisture leakage from the container due to excess water or condensation on the container surface.

2. Bark or gravel fill should be installed, if needed, to raise and level nursery pot to the proper height.

3. Free-water drainage should be provided for the plant root zone and a water siphon system installed, if necessary.

4. Plastic saucer and nursery-potted plant should be placed into the container or planter with pot rim no more than one inch below the edge of the container or planter.

5. Space(s) between nursery pot and container or planter should be filled with suitable fill material.

6. Container or planter should be top-dressed so fill material and pot rim(s) do not show.

See Detail on the Next Page

143

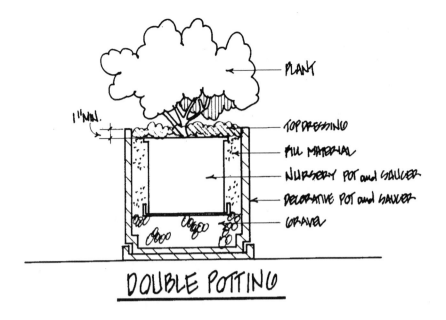

PLANT

1" MIN.

TOP DRESSING

FILL MATERIAL

NURSERY POT and SAUCER

DECORATIVE POT and SAUCER

GRAVEL

DOUBLE POTTING

B. DOUBLE POTTING IN SOIL-FILLED CONTAINER

Placement of plant in its nursery-grown pot directly into planting medium filled container or planter to allow for ease of rotation or replacement of plant.

1. Container or planter should be lined.

2. A layer of gravel should be placed in bottom of container or planter to provide a catch basin for drainage. A water siphon tube should be installed, if required.

3. A sheet of filter fabric (soil separator) should be placed on top of gravel and container or planter filled with planting medium. Level of planting medium should be one inch below top of container or planter when plant placement is complete.

4. Plant should be placed, in nursery-grown pot, directly into planting medium with rim of pot no more than one inch below the edge of the container or planter.

5. The container or planter should be top-dressed.

C. DIRECT POTTING

Planting of plants directly into soil-filled container or planter.

1. Container or planter should be lined.

2. Gravel should be placed and a water siphon tube installed, if required.

3. Filter fabric should be placed on top of the gravel and container filled with planting medium.

4. Plant should be removed from nursery pot and installed in planting medium with top of root ball one inch below edge of container or planter. Plant should not be placed deeper than it was growing in the grow-pot.

5. Container should be top-dressed.

See Detail on the Next Page

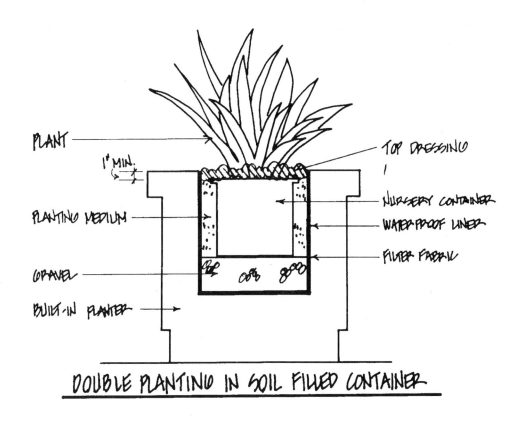

PLANT

1" MIN.

PLANTING MEDIUM

GRAVEL

BUILT-IN PLANTER

TOP DRESSING

NURSERY CONTAINER

WATERPROOF LINER

FILTER FABRIC

DOUBLE PLANTING IN SOIL FILLED CONTAINER

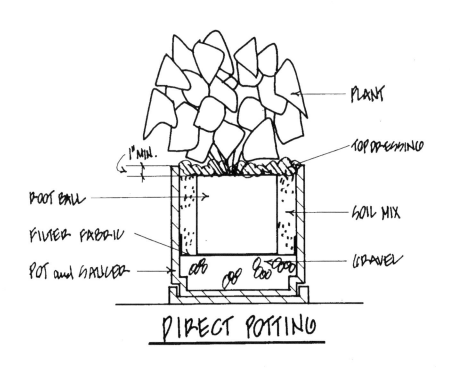

1" MIN.

ROOT BALL

FILTER FABRIC

POT and SAUCER

PLANT

TOP DRESSING

SOIL MIX

GRAVEL

DIRECT POTTING

145

D. CONTROLLED WATERING CONTAINERS

These containers provide integral systems allowing for the self-watering of plants.

1. Plants should be installed per manufacturer's recommendations.

2. Containers should be top-dressed.

3.04 IRRIGATION SYSTEMS
A. BUILT-IN PLANTERS

Installation of irrigation systems in this type of planter is frequently done when the planter is constructed.

B. DECORATIVE FREESTANDING CONTAINERS

The installation of irrigation systems in these types of containers is generally limited to drip irrigation.

C. INSTALLATION PROCEDURES
REFER TO IRRIGATION - PART 3

3.05 MAINTENANCE

Proper maintenance of interiorscapes should include the cleaning and trimming of plant foliage, necessary pruning, plant rotation, irrigation system management, drainage monitoring, watering, fertilization, disease and pest control, and removal of debris from decorative containers and built-in planters.

A. PLANT MATERIALS

Foliage should be periodically cleaned, trimmed, and yellow leaves removed to maintain an attractive appearance and the health of the plants.

1. Pruning should be done only as required to maintain attractive shape, form, and height.

2. As older foliage deteriorates, leaves should be removed.

3. Plants should be periodically rotated (turned) if in movable containers or double potted in built-in planters, to expose all sides to equal lighting conditions. When manually watered, plants should be rotated one-quarter turn at each watering.

B. IRRIGATION SYSTEMS

All non-pressure water lines, outlets, valves, and scheduling of controllers should be maintained.

C. DRAINAGE MONITORING

1. All containers and planters should be checked for excess standing water at least once monthly.

2. Plants should not be allowed to sit in more than 1/4 inch of standing water.

3. Excess water should be siphoned from containers and planters, as required for the health of the plants.

D. WATERING

1. Plant material should be properly watered in order to maintain proper foliage turgidity and ensure proper plant health.

2. Plants should be checked weekly with a tensiometer, to evaluate watering needs.

3. Frequency of watering, manually or with irrigation systems, should be scheduled to maintain proper moisture content in the root zone area without causing water logging and/or poorly aerated root zone medium.

E. DEBRIS REMOVAL

All leaves and other debris should be removed from containers and planters weekly.

F. FERTILIZATION

A well-defined supplemental fertilizer program should be developed based on plant type and species, available light, temperature, and container size.

1. Fertilizer should be applied, based on the specific requirements of the plant material, at one-half the manufacturer's recommended application rate.

2. Applications should be made a minimum of three times per year (spring, summer and fall), based on individual plant needs.

3. Long-term, slow-release fertilizers may be used.

4. Strict consideration should be given to maintaining proper pH levels (6.0-6.5) and soluble salt levels of not more than 700 ppm.

G. DISEASE AND PEST CONTROL

A complete and continuous monitoring/inspection program to detect disease and pest problems should be maintained.

1. It is difficult to control and eradicate diseases and pests in the interior environment. Removal and replacement of the afflicted plant is recommended. If spraying is necessary, the plant should be moved to the outdoors, sprayed, and allowed to dry thoroughly before the plant is returned indoors. On-site spraying must be done with utmost caution.

2. Insecticidal soaps should be used whenever possible.

3. Specific pesticides (insecticides and fungicides) should be chosen with utmost care and concern for public safety, and to minimize exposure of the public or public areas to noxious odors, cosmetic blemishes, and other physically irritating factors.

4. Any and all chemicals used MUST be registered in the State of California for INDOOR USE and MUST be applied under the strict supervision of a licensed and qualified pest control applicator, per the manufacturer's specific instructions and the regulations of governing agencies.

H. PLANT REPLACEMENT

Any plant removed from the site because of disease or pest problems should be replaced at the time of removal with a like plant.

Minimum Post Sizes[1] (Wood Beam Supports)

Species Group[2]	Post Sizes (inches)	Load area[3] beam spacing x post spacing (sq. ft.)									
		36	48	60	72	84	96	108	120	132	144
One	4 x 4	Up to 12 ft. heights ⟶				Up to 10 ft. heights		Up to 8 ft. heights			
	4 x 6					Up to 12 ft. heights ⟶				Up to 10 ft.	
	6 x 6									Up to 12 ft.	
Two	4 x 4	Up to 12 ft.		Up to 10 ft. heights			Up to 8 ft. heights ⟶				
	4 x 6			Up to 12 ft. heights			Up to 10 ft. heights ⟶				
	6 x 6							Up to 12 ft. heights ⟶			
Three	4 x 4	Up to 10 ft. heights		Up to 8 ft. heights			Up to 6 ft. heights ⟶				
	4 x 6		Up to 12 ft.		Up to 10 ft. heights		Up to 8 ft. heights ⟶				
	6 x 6				Up to 12 ft. heights ⟶						

[1] Based on 40 p.s.f. deck live load plus 10 p.s.f. dead load. Grade is Standard and Better for 4x4" posts and No. 1 and Better for larger sizes.

[2] Group 1 — Douglas-fir-larch and southern pine; Group 2 — Hem-fir and Douglas-fir-south; Group 3 — Western pines and cedars, redwood, and spruces.

[3] Example: If the beam supports are spaced 8'6" on center and the posts are 11'6" on center, then the load area is 98. Use next larger area 108.

Beam Sizes (Joist Spans)[1]

Species Group[2]	Beam Sizes (inches)	Beam Spacing[3] (ft.) (Joist Span)								
		4	5	6	7	8	9	10	11	12
One	4 x 6	Up to 6 ft. spans →								
	3 x 8	Up to 8 ft. spans		Up to 7 ft.	Up to 6 ft. spans →					
	4 x 8	Up to 10 ft.	Up to 9 ft.	Up to 8 ft.	Up to 7 ft. →		Up to 6 ft. spans →			
	3 x 10	Up to 11 ft.	Up to 10 ft.	Up to 9 ft.	Up to 8 ft. →		Up to 7 ft. →		Up to 6 ft. →	
	4 x 10	Up to 12 ft.	Up to 11 ft.	Up to 10 ft.	Up to 9 ft. →		Up to 8 ft. →		Up to 7 ft. →	
	3 x 12		Up to 12 ft.	Up to 11 ft.	Up to 10 ft.	Up to 9 ft. →		Up to 8 ft. →		
	4 x 12			Up to 12 ft. →		Up to 11 ft.	Up to 10 ft.		Up to 9 ft. →	
	6 x 10					Up to 12 ft.	Up to 11 ft.	Up to 10 ft. →		
Two	4 x 6	Up to 6 ft. →								
	3 x 8	Up to 7 ft. →		Up to 6 ft. →						
	4 x 8	Up to 9 ft.	Up to 8 ft.	Up to 7 ft. →		Up to 6 ft. →				
	3 x 10	Up to 10 ft.	Up to 9 ft.	Up to 8 ft.	Up to 7 ft. →		Up to 6 ft. →			
	4 x 10	Up to 11 ft.	Up to 10 ft.	Up to 9 ft.	Up to 8 ft. →		Up to 7 ft. →			Up to 6 ft.
	3 x 12	Up to 12 ft.	Up to 11 ft.	Up to 10 ft.	Up to 9 ft.	Up to 8 ft. →		Up to 7 ft. →		
	4 x 12		Up to 12 ft.	Up to 11 ft.	Up to 10 ft. →		Up to 9 ft. →		Up to 8 ft. →	
	6 x 10			Up to 12 ft.	Up to 11 ft.	Up to 10 ft. →		Up to 9 ft. →		
Three	4 x 6	Up to 6 ft.								
	3 x 8	Up to 7 ft.	Up to 6 ft.							
	4 x 8	Up to 8 ft.	Up to 7 ft.	Up to 6 ft. →						
	3 x 10	Up to 9 ft.	Up to 8 ft.	Up to 7 ft.	Up to 6 ft. →					
	4 x 10	Up to 10 ft.	Up to 9 ft.	Up to 8 ft. →		Up to 7 ft. →		Up to 6 ft. →		
	3 x 12	Up to 11 ft.	Up to 10 ft.	Up to 9 ft.	Up to 8 ft.	Up to 7 ft. →			Up to 6 ft. →	
	4 x 12	Up to 12 ft.	Up to 11 ft.	Up to 10 ft.	Up to 9 ft. →		Up to 8 ft. →		Up to 7 ft. →	
	6 x 10		Up to 12 ft.	Up to 11 ft.	Up to 10 ft.	Up to 9 ft. →		Up to 8 ft. →		

[1] Beams are on edge. Spans are center to center distances between posts or supports. (Based on 40 p.s.f. deck live load plus 10 p.s.f dead load. Grade is No. 2 or Better; No. 2, medium grain southern pine.)

[2] Group 1 — Douglas-fir-larch and southern pine; Group 2 — Hem-fir and Douglas-fir-south; Group 3 — Western pines and cedars, redwood, and spruces.

[3] Example: If the beam supports are spaced 9'8" apart and the species is Group 2, use the 10-foot column; 3 x 10 up to 6 ft. spans, 4 x10 up to 7 ft., etc.

Joist Spacing[1] (Decking Span)

Species Group[2]	Joist Sizes (inches)	Joist Spacing (inches)		
		16	24	32
One	2 x 6	9' 9"	7' 11"	6' 2"
	2 x 8	12' 10"	10' 6"	8' 1"
	2 x 10	16' 5"	13' 4"	10' 4"
Two	2 x 6	8' 7"	7' 0"	5' 8"
	2 x 8	11' 4"	9' 3"	7' 6"
	2 x 10	14' 6"	11' 10"	9' 6"
Three	2 x 6	7' 9"	6' 2"	5' 0"
	2 x 8	10' 2"	8' 1"	6' 8"
	2 x 10	13' 0"	10' 4"	8' 6"

[1] Joints are on edge. Spans are center to center distances between beams or supports. Based on 40 p.s.f. deck live load plus 10 p.s.f dead load. Grade is No. 2 or Better; No. 2 medium grain southern pine.

[2] Group 1 — Douglas-fir-larch and southern pine; Group 2 — Hem-fir and Douglas-fir-south; Group 3 — Western pines and cedars, redwood, and spruces.

Maximum allowable spans for spaced deck boards[1]

Species Group[2]	Maximum Allowable Span[3] (inches)					
	Laid Flat				Laid On Edge	
	1 x 4	2 x 2	2 x 3	2 x 4	2 x 3	2 x 4
One	16	60	60	60	90	144
Two	14	48	48	48	78	120
Three	12	42	42	42	66	108

[1] These spans are based on the assumption that more than one floor board carries normal loads. If concentrated loads are a rule, spans should be reduced accordingly.

[2] Group 1 — Douglas-fir-larch and southern pine; Group 2 — Hem-fir and Douglas-fir-south; Group 3 — Western pines and cedars, redwood, and spruces.

[3] Based on Construction grade or Better (Select Structural, Appearance, No. 1 or No. 2).

ABS PIPE. Abbreviation for acrylonitrile-butadiene-styrene. A black, semi-rigid, plastic pipe. Fittings are solvent welded.

AC. Abbreviation for asphalt concrete.

ACID SOIL. Soils with a pH level below 6.0.

ACID WASH. A combination of muriatic acid (HCL) and water used to clean cement or mortar stains on concrete and masonry work.

ADMIXTURES. As a concrete term, ingredients other than portland cement, aggregates, and water. These include air entraining agents, colorants, or retardants.

AIR-DRIED. Lumber that has been allowed to season in the air rather than dried in a kiln. Air-dried lumber contains approximately 19% moisture.

AIR POCKET. A cavity in a concrete mass that may be eliminated by tamping, vibrating, or tapping the forms.

ALKALINE SOILS. Soils with a pH level above 7.3.

AMPERE. A unit of measure of the flow of electrical current through a wire or conductor.

AMENDMENT. Any material added to the soil to alter the pH or improve the physical properties of the soil.

ANGLE VALVE. A valve from which the water discharges at a 90-degree angle from the plane at which it entered.

ANTI-SIPHON VALVE. A valve that allows water to flow in only one direction. It prevents the water in an irrigation system from flowing into the domestic water supply.

APPLICATION RATE. In irrigation, the rate, inches, or gallons per week at which water is applied by an irrigation system.

ARC. The degree of coverage of a sprinkler head from one side of throw to the other.

AREA DRAIN. A drain used to collect water from a specific area which is connected directly to an underground pipe.

AREA LIGHTING. The lighting of large garden areas.

AS-BUILT DRAWINGS. Drawings prepared after completion of work to show accurately all alterations made during construction.

ASPHALT CONCRETE. A high quality, thoroughly controlled, hot mixture of asphaltic cement and well-graded mineral aggregate.

ASTM. Abbreviation for American Society for Testing Materials. An organization involved in establishing quality standards for a wide variety of materials. Often referred to in specifications.

ATMOSPHERIC VACUUM BREAKER. A backflow prevention device which is vented to the atmosphere and installed on the non-pressure side of a control valve.

AUTOMATIC CONTROL VALVE. A valve in an irrigation system which is activated by an automatic electric controller via an electric control wire.

AUTOMATIC IRRIGATION SYSTEM. An irrigation system that can be controlled without manual manipulation and which operates on a preset program.

AVAILABLE WATER. The amount of water held in the root zone of a plant, between field capacity and the wilting point.

BACKFILL. The replacement of excavated material around a structure, in trenches, or in plant hole excavations. Also used to define the material itself.

BACKFLOW PREVENTER. A mechanical device which allows water to flow in one direction and restricts water flow in the opposite direction.

BACKPRESSURE. Occurs when a water user's system is at a higher pressure than the water supply system which allows undesirable substances to be pushed back into the potable water system.

BACKSIPHONAGE. Occurs when negative or reduced pressure exists in the water supply piping, which allows undesirable substances to be drawn into the potable water supply.

BATTER. To slope back from the base. Stone and other types of walls are often constructed with a batter.

BEAM. A heavy, horizontal timber that usually supports joists.

BENCH MARK. A permanent mark or reference point used as an elevation reference in surveying.

BENDER BOARD. A very thin (1/4 to 1/2 inch) board used to form curved header boards or dividers. Bender board is usually redwood.

BERM. (1) An elongated mound. (2) A narrow space or ledge. (3) The shoulder of a road or the gradual transition slope around a paved area. (4) The edge of the watering basin around a plant.

BEVEL. To cut on a slant so the angle formed is not a rigid angle.

BLOCKING. In deck construction, pieces of solid wood connecting joists, to improve load distribution.

BOARD FOOT. In lumber measurement, a piece of lumber measuring 1 x 12 x 12 inches equals one board foot.

BOOSTER PUMP. A pump designed to raise the existing water pressure in an irrigation system.

BRICK PAVING. A commonly used paving surface. Bricks may be laid with or without mortar.

BROOM FINISH. A non-slip texture applied to freshly troweled concrete by pulling a damp broom across the concrete. Sidewalks and driveways are broomed at right angles to the direction of travel.

BUBBLER. A sprinkler head designed to emit water without spray.

BUSHING. In irrigation installations, a fitting used to change the type and/or size of a connection.

BUTT JOINT. The joint where two wood members come together end to end.

CALIPER. In landscape and nursery usage, the diameter of a tree trunk. Trees of four-inch caliper or less are measured six inches above the ground. Calipers over four inches are measured 12 inches above the ground.

CANDLEPOWER. The illuminating power of a standard candle, used as a measure of other illuminants.

CANTILEVER. A projecting beam or member supported at one end.

CAPILLARY ACTION. Attraction of water molecules to soil particles which causes the upward or downward movement of water into the soil.

CATCH BASIN. A drainage structure used to collect water from a specific area which contains a pit to collect sediment.

CENTER LINE. A set of points along the center of a road, pipeline, ditch, or other improvement or structure.

CHAMPFER. A beveled edge on a piece of wood.

CHECK VALVE. A valve designed to permit flow of water in only one direction. Check valves rely upon seat weight or spring force to remain closed against the reverse flow of water.

CHLOROSIS. The loss of normal green color in a plant caused by the loss of chlorophyll.

CIRCUIT. (1) In irrigation systems, all of the pipe and components downstream from a valve. (2) In electrical systems, the path of electrical current leading from a power source, to electrical switches and outlets, and back to the source.

CLASS. The basic service rating for PVC pipe. Class is expressed as the maximum operating pressure. Typical ratings are 160, 200, and 315 psi.

COMPACTION. To compress a material, such as sub-base, to increase the load bearing capacity.

COMPLETE FERTILIZER. Fertilizers containing the three primary mineral elements (nitrogen, phosphorus, potassium) considered necessary for plant growth.

CONCRETE. A mixture of portland cement, coarse and fine aggregates, and water. Concrete may include admixtures.

CONCRETE BUILDING BLOCK. A concrete masonry unit formed with cells.

CONDUCTOR. A material which offers little resistance to the flow of electric current.

CONDUIT. As an electrical term, a pipe used to enclose wires and cables for protection.

CONTROLLED-RELEASE FERTILIZER. Fertilizers which release their nutrients over a long period of time.

CONTROLLER. An automatic timing device with enclosure, which signals automatic valves to open and close on a preset program.

CONTROL JOINT. A tooled or cut joint installed in concrete to induce cracking to occur beneath the groove and along the line. Also called contraction joint.

CONTOUR. A line drawn on a plan which connects all points to equal elevation above or below a known or assumed reference point.

CONTOUR INTERVAL. The difference in elevation from one contour line to another.

COPING. In masonry work, the covering course of a wall. Also the edge of a swimming pool.

COUPLING. A type of pipe fitting that joins two pieces of pipe of the same size and material together.

COVERAGE. A general term, used with respect to the spacing of sprinkler heads, which defines the manner in which water is applied.

CREEP. The slow movement of soil down a slope under the force of gravity.

CROSS-CONNECTION. Any point on a water system where a potential polluting substance may come in contact with a potable water supply.

CSI. Abbreviation for Construction Specification Institute.

CUBIC YARD. The typical unit of measurement for earthwork, or gravel, sand, and other materials.

CULVERT. An underground pipe used to carry water by gravity flow.

CURING. Used as a concrete term, maintaining the moist, warm conditions under which concrete hardens.

CURING PERIOD. Usually five days in warm weather and seven days in cooler weather. Strength tests are taken at 28 days.

CURING COMPOUNDS. Compounds used to cure concrete.

CURRENT. The flow of electricity through a conductor measured in amperes.

CUT AND FILL. Grading operations which change the contours of the land by moving soil from one area and placing it in another.

CYCLE. In irrigation, the complete operation of a controller station.

DEAD LOAD. A term common to deck design. The fixed and permanent load on a beam from the weight of the decking material and other parts of the structure, Also referred to as static load.

DEADMAN. An anchor or heavy mass buried in the earth to anchor and provide additional strength in a retaining wall. Also used to guy trees.

DECK. A wooden structure constructed above ground. Decks are often attached to a building to extend the interior living space.

DF. Abbreviation for Douglas fir.

DRAIN VALVE. A valve located at a low point in the irrigation system, which allows the laterals, valves, and main line to be drained for winterization of the system.

DRIP IRRIGATION. Low volume irrigation.

DRIP-LINE. The line directly under the outermost ends of the branches of a plant.

DRY MASONRY WALL. A stone wall built without mortar joints.

EFFLORESCENCE. A crust of soluble salts on the surface of concrete, brick, stone, mortar, or plaster caused by free alkalines leached from the concrete or mortar as moisture passes through the masonry.

ELECTRIC DIAPHRAGM VALVE. A remote control valve used in irrigation systems, operated by an electrically actuated hydraulic valve.

ELEVATION. The level of a certain point above or below a reference point such as sea level.

ELL. A pipe fitting used to allow 45- or 90-degree turns when installing piping.

EMITTER. A device used in drip irrigation, to reduce the water pressure within the lateral line to a minimum prior to discharging water into the soil.

EROSION. The wearing away of land surfaces by loosening and movement of soils caused by water or wind.

ESPALIER. Trees or shrubs trained to grow on a wall or framework.

EVAPORATION. The moisture loss from the soil.

EXCAVATION. A cavity formed by cutting, digging, or scooping. Typically for the purpose of footings and foundations.

EXPANSION BOLT. A bolt that can be enlarged once it is in place, to hold it firmly in the desired position. Frequently used as an anchor in masonry.

EXPANSION JOINT. A wood, metal, or other divider placed in concrete to allow movement where concrete abuts other structures or concrete slabs. Also called isolation joint.

EXPOSED AGGREGATE PAVING. A concrete paving surface in which the aggregate in the concrete is exposed for decorative purposes.

FACIA. A flat board used as a band or face at the top of a wall, or on the edge of a deck or bench.

FIELD CAPACITY. The amount of water retained in soil after the soil has been saturated and allowed to drain freely.

FILTER FABRIC. A manufactured non-woven geotextile fabric used in drainage applications.

FINAL GRADE. The grade which reestablishes the finish grade after all site improvements are completed.

FINISH GRADE. The grade established after all site preparation work is complete, which will allow for proper drainage across all surfaces of a site.

FITTINGS. A means of joining pieces of pipe together or connecting the pipe to other irrigation components.

FLAGSTONE. Any hard stone that has been split into thin pieces suitable for paving.

FLASHING. Sheet metal or other materials used to protect buildings from moisture seepage from adjoining structures.

FLEXIBLE RISER. An irrigation riser made from flexible material to prevent breakage.

FLOATING. A concrete finishing term. Following screeding, edging, and jointing, the surface of concrete is floated to embed the aggregate, remove imperfections, and compact the concrete. Floats may be wood, metal, or plastic.

FLUSH. (1) Unbroken or even in surface, on level with an adjacent surface. (2) To wash out with a flow of water.

FOOT-CANDLE. The unit for measuring the amount of illumination striking a surface.

FOOTING. A foundation or enlargement at the base of a wall, pier, or column wider than the structure it supports, for the purpose of distributing the load over a larger surface.

FORMAL PRUNING. The precise, smooth shearing of shrubs and hedges into distinct and/or uniform shapes.

FORMS. Wood, metal, or other materials used to hold concrete in place until set or hardened.

FORM RELEASE AGENT. Compounds used to allow forms to be stripped easily from concrete.

FRENCH DRAIN. A drainage ditch filled with gravel, which drains to a point of discharge. A drain pipe may be included.

FRICTION LOSS. The loss of water pressure in pipe and fittings caused by the friction between the flowing water and the walls of the pipe and fittings. Friction loss cannot occur unless the water is flowing.

FROST LINE. The depth to which frost will penetrate the ground. Footings are usually placed below the frost line.

GATE VALVE. A low friction loss valve. Gate valves are not used to throttle and are best left opened or closed.

GFI. Abbreviation for Ground Fault Interrupter. A safety device that interrupts a circuit in approximately 1/40 of a second if it detects any leakage of current, to prevent shock.

GIRDLING. An encircling clamping or cutting through the bark of a tree trunk or branch.

GLOBE VALVE. A control valve available in either straight or angle patterns.

GPM. Abbreviation for gallons per minute.

GRADE. (1) A particular elevation. (2) A term used frequently to indicate the desired elevation in grading operations. (3) To make level or properly inclined.

GRADE STAKES. Wooden stakes or markers used to indicate the desired grade or elevations, or cuts and fills.

GRADIENT. The rate of, or the percentage of, slope between two points.

GRADING. The moving of earth, by cut and fill, to create landforms.

GRAIN. The direction of the fibers in wood. Flat grain lumber is sawed parallel to the pitch, tangent to the growth rings, with the bark side up. Vertical grain lumber is sawed with the wide surfaces at right angles to the growth rings.

GROUT. A mixture of portland cement, sand, and water used to fill cavities in concrete building block construction.

GUSSET. A flat wooden member used to connect the intersection of two boards.

HEAD. A slang term for a sprinkler head.

HEADER BOARD. Board(s) buried in the ground used as a divider or edging around planting beds, paths, paving, or other areas.

HEADWALL. A vertical wall at a culvert or pipe, to prevent erosion and protect the end of the pipe.

HOSE BIB. A water outlet a hose can be attached to.

HYDROSEEDING/HYDROMULCHING. A hydraulic method of spraying a slurry mix of fiber, seed, and fertilizer onto slopes for erosion control measures.

I.D. The inside diameter of a pipe.

IMPACT DRIVE. A type of sprinkler head in which a spring-loaded drive is deflected by the force of the water, causing the rotation of the sprinkler head.

IMPERVIOUS SOIL. Soil which provides very little percolation properties.

INFORMAL. Used as a pruning term, plants pruned naturally and allowed to attain their normal growth pattern.

IRRIGATION SYSTEM. A complete connection of system components, including the water source, the water distribution network, and the necessary irrigation equipment.

INSULATOR. A material that does not conduct electricity.

INVERT. The flow line elevation of a pipe, drain inlet, or channel.

IPS. Abbreviation for iron pipe size.

JOISTS. Parallel boards used to support floor or ceiling loads. Joists are supported by beams, girders, or ceiling walls.

JOIST HANGERS. A galvanized metal stirrup used to connect joists to beams or other bearing members.

KILN DRIED. Lumber that has been dried by artificial means. Kiln dried lumber is used in situations where shrinkage cannot be tolerated. Kiln dried lumber contains approximately 5% to 7% moisture.

LANDING. A platform dividing two flights of stairs.

LATERAL. (1) In irrigation usage, the pipe downstream from the control valve on which the sprinkler heads are located. (2) A branch attached to the leader or trunk of a tree or shrub.

LEACHING. The removal of soluble mineral deposits in the soil by percolation of water through the soil.

LEADER. A developing stem in a tree or shrub that is longer and more vigorous than the laterals.

LEDGER. A strip of lumber attached to a girder or joist that other joists are placed upon. A heavy board attached to a wall or foundation as a joist support.

LIFT. A layer of fill or paving material.

LIVE LOAD. In deck construction, any weight placed on the deck other than the dead load or static load, such as people, furniture, or snow.

LOAM. Soil which has a relatively uneven mixture of various grades of sand, silt, and clay.

LUMEN. A unit for measuring the amount of light emitted by a lamp.

MAIN. (1) A water supply line that is under constant pressure. (2) An electrical supply line.

MASONRY. Concrete block, brick, stone, or tile construction.

MASTER VALVE. A normally closed valve installed at the water supply point of connection to the irrigation main, which opens only when an automatic irrigation system is activated.

MITER. A cut made at an angle, usually a 45-degree angle. The term also refers to joining two pieces together at an evenly divided angle.

MORTAR. A mixture of cement, lime, sand, and water used to lay masonry units, and for plaster and stucco coats.

MOW STRIP. An edging, usually concrete, between lawn and planting areas.

MULCH. Materials such as bark or sawdust placed on the soil surface to retain moisture, retard weed growth, or prevent erosion.

MURATIC ACID. An acid compound used to clean cement stains from masonry work.

NATURAL GRADE. The undisturbed surface of the terrain.

NATURAL STONE. Stone left uncut and used in the natural form.

NIPPLE. A short piece of pipe pre-threaded on both ends, used as both fittings and risers.

NOMINAL SIZE. (1) The size lumber is before it is planed. (2) Dimensions for masonry units.

NORMALLY CLOSED VALVE. An automatic valve through which no water will flow unless externally activated by electric or hydraulic forces.

NORMALLY OPEN VALVE. An automatic valve through which water will flow freely unless external electric or hydraulic forces are applied to close the valve.

NUTRIENT. An element or substance which contributes to healthy growth of plants.

O.C. Abbreviation for on center.

O.D. Abbreviation for outside diameter.

OPERATING PRESSURE. The pressure at which an irrigation system operates. Usually measured at the nozzle of a sprinkler head.

ORGANIC FERTILIZER. Organic matter which releases or supplies useful amounts of plant nutrients when added to the soil.

ORGANIC MATERIAL. Animal or plant material that will decompose in the soil.

OSHA. Abbreviation for Occupational Safety and Health Administration.

OWNER'S REPRESENTATIVE. An individual or company retained by an owner to oversee and/or inspect a project.

PAVING UNIT. Prefabricated units used for paving.

PEA GRAVEL. Small-diameter natural gravel screened to size.

PENNY. A size designation for nail length. A 16d nail Is 3-1/2 inches long.

PERCOLATION. The movement of water through the soil.

PERMEABILITY. The quality of a soil which allows water and air to pass through it.

pH. A designation of relative acidity or alkalinity in soils. A pH of 7.0 indicates neutral.

PIER. A column of concrete or masonry used to support heavy materials. Similar to a footing.

PIPE PULLING. A method of installing irrigation pipe with a special machine that pulls the pipe through the ground without trenching.

PLANT AVAILABLE MOISTURE. Water held loosely enough in the soil to allow plants to extract the water for their use.

PLUMB. Perpendicular to level, exactly vertical in position.

POLYETHYLENE PIPE. A black, flexible pipe commonly used in drip and sprinkler irrigation systems.

PONDING. The build-up of water on a ground surface.

POP-UP SPRINKLER. A sprinkler that is flush with the ground when not in operation and rises above the ground when operational.

PORTLAND CEMENT. A dry powder mixture of lime, clay, and gypsum used as a binding material in concrete and mortar. Portland cement is not a brand name, but a type of cement.

POTABLE WATER. Water fit for human consumption.

PRECIPITATION RATE. The amount of water, in inches per hour, discharged by a group of sprinkler heads.

PRE-EMERGENT. Chemicals used to prevent the germination of seeds.

PRESSURE LOSS. The loss of water pressure energy under flow conditions caused by elevation, pipe friction, or directional changes within the irrigation piping.

PRESSURE REGULATOR. A device which regulates the available water pressure to a preset maximum under static or flow conditions.

PRESSURE TREATED. A chemical treatment of lumber to preserve lumber.

PSI. Abbreviation for pounds per square inch. Water pressure is measured in psi.

PVC. Abbreviation for unplasticized polyvinyl chloride. A commonly used material in the manufacture of irrigation pipe.

QUARRIED STONE. Stone that has been dug from a quarry.

QUICK COUPLER. A valve with a spring-loaded seat, which is forced open manually by a coupler key.

REBAR. Slang term for reinforcing rods used in concrete and masonry construction.

REINFORCING STEEL. Steel rods of various sizes used in concrete or masonry to provide reinforcement. Standard length is 20 feet. May be referred to as rods, bars, or rebar.

RETAINING WALL. A wall built to retain an embankment or a change in surface levels.

RETARDANT. A chemical agent added to concrete, to slow the hardening process.

READY MIX. Previously mixed concrete delivered to the site.

RIP-RAP. Irregularly shaped broken stone generally used to prevent erosion on the face of slopes.

RISER. The vertical surface of a step from tread to tread.

RISER PIPE. A pipe used to raise a sprinkler head above the ground.

ROCK SALT FINISH. A concrete finish obtained by embedding rock salt in the surface of freshly troweled concrete. The salt is removed after the concrete hardens.

ROOT BOUND. Used to describe a condition of container-grown plants when the roots have grown together. Usually occurs when plants have remained in the same size container too long.

ROUGH GRADING. The preliminary earthwork that precedes finish grading.

RUNNING BOND. A masonry term for masonry units laid so the joints on one course overlay the joints of the course below by one-half the length of the unit.

RUNOFF. Water which is not absorbed by the soil to which it is applied. Runoff usually occurs when water is applied at too great a rate or when water is applied to a steep slope.

RWD. Abbreviation for redwood.

S4S. Abbreviation of surfaced four sides. Lumber that has been planed on all four sides.

SALINITY. The level of salts in the soil. Excessive levels can be damaging to plant material.

SAND. Soil particles which can be seen with the naked eye and can be felt as individual grains.

SANDBLASTING. The use of sand propelled by an air gun, to clean dirt or rust from a surface. In some cases it may be used to decorate a surface.

SANDY LOAM. A soil consisting predominately of sand particles having enough silt and clay particles to make it cohesive.

SATURATION. The condition of a soil when all soil pores are filled with water.

SCORE. To mark with lines or scratches.

SCH. Abbreviation for schedule.

SCHEDULE. A service rating for pipe based on wall thickness of the pipe.

SCREEDING. The initial leveling of concrete after it has been poured.

SDR. Abbreviation for Standard Dimension Ratio. A formula for making the wall thickness in the same ratio to the outside diameter of a given pipe in all sizes, to obtain uniform working pressures throughout any class.

SERVICE LINE. (1) In irrigation, the pipe that connects the structure or facility to the water meter. (2) In electrical uses, the line that provides service to the structure or facility.

SHOP DRAWINGS. Drawings prepared to show proposed methods of construction.

SHRINKAGE FACTOR. The tendency of fill material to decrease in volume due to compaction or wetting. Soils may shrink 0% to 30%.

SLIP FITTING. A fitting which is solvent welded to PVC or ABS pipe.

SILT. Soil particles which appear and feel like flour.

SITE PLAN. A plan showing the features, contours, and dimensions of a plot of land, along with the location and dimensions of elements to be constructed.

SLEEVE. A conduit for pipe or wires.

SLOPE RATIO. The relation of the horizontal distance to the vertical rise and fall.

SLUMPSTONE. A concrete masonry unit molded with two slumped sides.

SNAP VALVE. Same as quick coupler.

SOIL AMENDMENTS. Any material such as ground bark or other conditioners worked into the soil, to change the soil characteristics.

SOIL CEMENT. A type of paving surface where cement is blended into the soil, wet thoroughly, and then compacted.

SOIL STABILIZATION. The treatment of soil to provide protection against erosion.

SOLDER. A tin plus lead alloy with a very low melting point, used for welding.

SOLVENT. A product which causes a partial dissolving of PVC or ABS pipe and fittings, allowing for a chemical fusion of the pipe and fittings.

SOLVENT WELD. The chemical fusing of pipe and fittings.

SPLASH BLOCK. A block placed beneath a stream of flowing water, to catch the flow and prevent erosion. Often used under rain gutter downspouts.

SPOIL. Surplus earth or other materials from an excavation.

STATIC PRESSURE. The pressure in an irrigation system when the water is not flowing.

STATION. A position on an automatic irrigation controller which indicates the control point of automatic irrigation valves.

STREET ELL. A pipe fitting identical to an ell with one male end and one female end.

STRETCHER. A masonry unit laid with its longest dimension parallel to the run of the course.

STRINGER. (1) A support for cross members in floors or ceilings. (2) The supports on which stair treads rest. (3) The boards used to connect the posts in fence construction.

SUB-GRADE. The surface of graded native soil on which fill, topsoil, or sub-base materials are placed, or upon which foundations and other improvements are constructed.

SUB-SURFACE DRAIN. The collection of water utilizing gravel-filled ditches to intercept the flow of water with, or without, perforated drain pipe used to transport the water.

SURFACE DRAINAGE. The collection of water, utilizing swales, gutters, catch basins, and area drains, which is then channeled through a piping system to the disposal area.

SUMP. A reservoir used to collect drainage water.

SURCHARGE. An excessive load or burden. Used in describing retaining walls where the earth is sloped above the top level of the wall.

SURGE. An energy wave in pipe lines caused by sudden opening or closing of valves. Also referred to as a water hammer.

SWALE. A depression in grade, to control the flow of surface water.

SWING CHECK VALVE. A valve which allows water flow in only one direction. Closure against a backflow is provided by the weight of the pendulum action seat.

SWING JOINT. An irrigation term for a type of connection used to attach risers to supply lines, which allows for adjustment of height and angle, and provides flex to protect the pipe.

TEE. A pipe fitting with three outlets.

TENSIOMETER. An instrument for measuring the moisture content of the soil.

TIE-BACK. Same as deadman.

TOE-NAILING. Nails driven at an angle.

TOE OF SLOPE. The base of a slope, the bottom edge.

TOP OF SLOPE. The upper terminus of a slope.

TRANSPIRATION. The process by which a plant removes water from the soil, moves the water to its leaves, and transpires moisture into the atmosphere.

TREAD. The horizontal board in a stairway.

TREE WELL. A pit built around the base of a tree when the grade is raised around it so the original grade may be preserved at the crown of the tree.

VACUUM BREAKER. A device used to prevent water in an irrigation system from siphoning into the domestic water supply.

VALVE-UNDER-HEAD. A sprinkler in which the valve and sprinkler head are one unit. The valve is located just below the sprinkler head.

VELOCITY. The speed at which water travels.

VOLT. A unit of measure of electrical pressure.

WATER PRESSURE. The pressure water exerts as measured in pounds per square inch or in head feet.

WATTS. A unit of measure of electrical power.

WEEP HOLE. A drainage hole installed in retaining walls and other structures.

WOOD PRESERVATIVES. A class of chemicals used to prevent or retard the decay of wood, especially by fungi or insects. Particularly important for wood used in ground contact.

WORKING PRESSURE. The pressure in an irrigation system when it is operational. Working pressure is always lower than static pressure due to friction loss.

WYTHE. A masonry term which refers to the thickness of a wall. A wall one brick thick is a single wythe wall.

AMERICAN SOCIETY FOR TESTING AND MATERIALS Philadelphia, PA 19103
VARIOUS BULLETINS

CALIFORNIA DEPARTMENT OF FOOD AND AGRICULTURE Sacramento, CA 95814
CALIFORNIA FOOD AND AGRICULTURE CODE

CALIFORNIA REDWOOD ASSOCIATION Novato, CA 94949
VARIOUS PUBLICATIONS

INTERNATIONAL CONFERENCE OF BUILDING OFFICIALS Whittier, CA 90601
UNIFORM BUILDING CODE

INTERNATIONAL CONFERENCE OF PLUMBING AND MECHANICAL OFFICIALS
Los Angeles, CA 90032
UNIFORM PLUMBING CODE

STATE OF CALIFORNIA DEPARTMENT OF TRANSPORTATION Sacramento, CA
95819
CALTRANS STANDARD SPECIFICATIONS

STATE OF CALIFORNIA DOCUMENTS SECTIONS North Highlands, CA 95660
CALIFORNIA CONTRACTORS LICENSE LAW AND REFERENCE BOOK

SUNSET BOOKS, LANE PUBLISHING COMPANY Menlo Park, CA 94025
SUNSET WESTERN GARDEN BOOK

NATIONAL FIRE PROTECTION ASSOCIATION Quincy, MA 02169
NATIONAL ELECTRIC CODE

ORTHO BOOKS, CHEVRON CHEMICAL COMPANY San Ramon, CA 94583
HOW TO DESIGN & BUILD DECKS & PATIOS

PORTLAND CEMENT ASSOCIATION
Skokie, IL 60076
VARIOUS PUBLICATIONS

PUBLICATION DIVISION OF AGRICULTURE & NATURAL RESOURCES UNIVER-
SITY OF CALIFORNIA Oakland, CA 94608
AGRICULTURAL PUBLICATIONS

WESTERN WOOD PRESERVERS INSTITUTE Vancouver, WA 98668
VARIOUS PUBLICATIONS

WESTERN WOOD PRODUCTS ASSOCIATION Portland, OR 97204
VARIOUS PUBLICATIONS